LOTTIE MOON
and the
SILENT BELL

Rosalie Hall Hunt

ROSALIE HALL HUNT

100 Manly Street
Greenville, South Carolina 29601
CourierPublishing.com

PUBLISHED IN THE UNITED STATES OF AMERICA

Praise for
Lottie Moon and the Silent Bell

Rosalie has done it again. She has brought Lottie Moon to life for us all. As you read Lottie's story, you can feel the warmth of the fireplace, smell the cookies and see the twinkle in her eyes as she tells her stories. Children will love learning about this special lady.

Connie Dixon
President, Woman's Missionary Union

Thank you, Lord! Rosalie Hunt has made Baptist history come alive again. This time, she tells the story of a Baptist icon everyone thinks they know all about. As a former Sunbeam, RA and Baptist deacon, I know all about Lottie Moon — or I thought I did until I read Rosalie's book.

How I wish I could have been one of the Newton children who were able to sit at Lottie's feet and hear her tell her stories. You may feel the same way as you read this incredible story of a beloved Southern Baptist missionary who changed the direction of countless lives in China, in the US and around the world ... and still does today.

David George
President Emeritus, WMU Foundation

I can't imagine anyone sharing the intimate details of Lottie Moon's daily life other than our very own modern-day Lottie Moon: Rosalie Hall Hunt. How blessed we and future generations are that Rosalie has gifted us with this treasured account of one of our earliest missions heroes.

Jennifer Davis Rash
President and Editor-in-Chief
The Alabama Baptist and The Baptist Paper

Rosalie Hall Hunt creatively brings Lottie Moon to life. Each chapter unveils new adventures in China as Lottie shares her captivating mission stories with three of her favorite missionary kids. The reader will discover how God weaves His eternal purposes into our lives as we faithfully follow His mission call. God may very well use *Lottie Moon and the Silent Bell* to inspire readers to dream His dreams for their lives and become modern-day Lottie Moons.

Cindy Townsend
Minister to Women, First Baptist Church, Jackson, Mississippi
Former Executive Director of Missions and Ministry for the
Louisiana and Mississippi Baptist conventions

Although small in stature, Lottie Moon was a powerhouse for the Great Commission. She knew that God loved the people of China as much as He loved her, and the people of China didn't know that … yet.

What an opportunity *Lottie Moon and the Silent Bell* gives us to learn about one of our heroes of the faith from a missionary who lived in the same house as Lottie and gleaned information from someone who actually knew our beloved Lottie!

Rosalie Hall Hunt is a master at telling stories. May you feel "historical goosebumps" (Rosalie's words) as you read the firsthand account about the life of Lottie Moon from an author who is gifted at pulling you into the story. Grab a tea cookie and enjoy this book.

Linda Cooper, President, Kentucky WMU
President Emeritus, WMU (SBC)

This is a true story. It is an adventure story. Its truth has often helped people measure their lives by heavenly standards. It is timeless and can't be repeated often enough.

I want to thank Rosalie Hall Hunt for telling this old, old story in a fresh way. This account of Lottie Moon comes through the caring hands of a girl who grew up in China, hearing the true story of Lottie Moon. She is passing it on to you.

Catherine Allen
Baptist historian and advocate for women in mission
President Emeritus, Women's Department
of Baptist World Alliance

As I read this book, I felt like I was sitting at Aunt Lottie's feet with the Newton sisters and hearing these stories for the first time. Children will not only learn about what life was like for Lottie Moon, but they will also be challenged to consider their own role in the Great Commission. What an exciting adventure!

Heather Keller
WMU Mission Consultant for Girls in Action,
Children in Action, Acteens

Lottie Moon's life was poured out as a sacrificial offering to God. Her compelling story is an indispensable chapter spanning centuries of Baptist history. In this beautiful work, Rosalie Hall Hunt has honored Lottie Moon's legacy and blessed future generations with our revered heritage. Every child loves stories. Take some time to sit at Aunt Lottie's feet and hear her stories for yourself.

Sandy Wisdom-Martin
WMU Executive Director-Treasurer

I am so excited to endorse Rosalie's new book because it is Lottie Moon telling her life's adventures to three of her favorite MKs (missionaries' kids). The stories in *Lottie Moon and the Silent Bell* are all based on true events, but they also contain little-known facts about Lottie Moon herself.

I'm a huge fan of Rosalie's writing. I love the history and the "story" feel of each book she writes. This book will be a joy for you to read, but you will also be able to read the stories to your children or grandchildren, or to your GAs, RAs or Children in Action.

Ruby Fulbright
Former Executive Director/Treasurer, WMU North Carolina
Former Vice President, North American Baptist Women

DEDICATION

To David George, President Emeritus of
Woman's Missionary Union Foundation,
Who has, as did Lottie Moon, lived his calling
To share the good news

TABLE OF CONTENTS

FOREWORD

I am so excited for you to hear and read about this amazing missionary named Lottie Moon. My friend, Rosalie Hunt, has written this book, *Lottie Moon and the Silent Bell,* for you. Like me, she grew up as a missionary kid — except she actually grew up in China where missionary Lottie Moon served and worked for thirty-nine years. Rosalie has already written several books about missionaries. I loved her book *Bless God and Take Courage: The Judson History and Legacy* about Adoniram Judson who was a missionary to Burma — but Rosalie grew up in China, and I don't know of anyone who can tell Lottie Moon's story like she can. I think this book is going to be my favorite!

On one occasion I was visiting a church, and the pastor had just finished sharing the goal for the annual Lottie Moon missions offering when one of the church members raised his hand and asked: "When are we going to get that lady paid off?" Can you believe that, after all these years, there was someone in that church who had no clue who Lottie Moon was? Unfortunately, I'm pretty sure there are a lot more like him. They have never heard her story of giving her life to the Chinese people so that they could know Jesus.

After you read this lively, fascinating story, not only will you be inspired by her life, but you are going to help us keep telling people who Miss Lottie Moon was and how her example reminds us of how important it is to keep sending missionaries around the world to tell people about Jesus. There are a lot of problems in the world, but the greatest problem in our world today is lostness. People who have never heard about Jesus and who have never given their life to Him are spiritually lost. The only way many of them will ever hear the gospel is fsr somebody to go and tell them. That's why we need to tell the story of Miss Lottie Moon. We need for people to hear about her example and how she gave her life so that others could hear about Jesus.

I am so thankful that Rosalie Hunt has used her experience and skills to tell us this story. Unless we make sure that we are teaching every new generation about this incredible missionary and her life of dedicated service in China, we will get more and more people asking that question: "When are we going to get that lady paid off?" You are in for a real treat. This book is about to open your eyes and heart to an amazing lady and her story.

Dr. Gordon Fort
Senior Ambassador to the President
International Mission Board. SBC

PREFACE

Lottie Moon was a name often heard in our home when I was a missionary kid growing up in China. I vividly remember those long-ago years in the late 1940s. China was in turmoil and in the midst of civil war. We lived in Zhenjiang *(Juhn Jyahng)*, although foreigners called it Chinkiang. Years later, I learned that Lottie Moon had lived in our house in the summer of 1888. I like to think she and I shared the same bedroom!

Many years later in South Carolina, I found another link with the remarkable Miss Moon. I was visiting at Bethea Baptist Home in South Carolina, where my Aunt Grace lived. One afternoon, she took me to the apartment of ninety-five-year-old missionary Miss Jane Lide. "Miss Janie," as she was lovingly called, had spent her early years in north China being mentored and coached in Chinese customs, culture, and language. Who was her remarkable coach? None other than Lottie Moon.

As we visited, I realized Miss Janie's thinking seemed unclear. Then I decided to change languages. I spoke to her in Chinese, asking her about her years with Miss Moon. Her face lit up like a bright lightbulb was turned on. Miss Janie began telling me about her beloved friend, Lottie Moon. I felt such joy at feeling so closely linked to our missions history.

In 1996, this joy was renewed when I went to Shangdong Province and visited in Tengzhou *(Duhng Joe),* now called Penglai. I worshipped in Lottie Moon's home church, Monument Street Church. Just a block or so from there was her house at Little Crossroads. This was the kind of trip where I got "historical goosebumps," finding myself in the very places where pioneer missionary feet had walked and lived and worked.

In the morning worship service at Lottie's church, I met eighty-four-year-old Dr. Dan *(Dahn)*. Dr. Dan was the great-niece of Old Mr. Dan, the patriarch of Shaling village in the 1800s. Mr. Dan had heard about Jesus from the "Heavenly Book Visitor" (Miss Moon). Because of her, he had become a believer. Mr. Dan's great-niece told me, "How thankful I am that Miss Moon came to Shaling and told my family the way to eternal life."

The next day, I traveled to Pingtu *(Ping Do)* and visited Lottie Moon's house in the interior. I saw the brick *kang (kahng)* where she sat, day after day, and shared the good news with the many visitors who came. I also met Mr. Swun, the elderly owner of the house. He was born there in 1912, four years after Lottie Moon sailed for America. I treasure the little ornament from the roof that old Mr. Swun kindly gave me.

Shortly after my husband and I retired as IMB missionaries, I was asked to travel to the headquarters of the International Mission Board. They wanted help with examining documents from China. I worked with a retired Chinese Baptist leader from the Baptist seminary in north China. Mr. Ku served there many years with our missionaries. Ku Shien Sun *(Goo Sheann Shun*, or Mr. Ku) knew and loved Baptist missions. The two of us sorted through many boxes of old mission records and deeds from all over China.

I was excited to see the deed for our mission residence in Zhenjiang. From it, I learned that the house where I lived as a little girl dated back to the mid-1800s. Just as thrilling was seeing documents from Shantung *(Shandong)* Province, and records written by our early missionaries, including Miss Lottie Moon herself.

Beginning in the mid-1990s, I began doing a Lottie Moon monologue in churches at Christmas time. I dress as Lottie and use her own words to tell her story. This has been going on for many years now, and I can feel her words in my heart as I share them.

Lottie Moon and the Silent Bell digs into the details of Lottie Moon's life. It explores some little-known stories from her remarkable life of commitment to the people of China. They became her people.

This account also features three MKs (missionaries' kids). As I began writing this book, I realized that Rachel Newton, the oldest of the MKs who visited Lottie, was my own mother's personal friend. Mother (Alice Wells Hall) left for China right after her appointment as a missionary in 1929. Rachel Newton was on the same ship with her, returning to China for her second term as a missionary! Rachel and Alice remained lifelong friends.

Let's journey together to China in our minds and discover an important piece of our Baptist missions history. *Lottie Moon and the Silent Bell* finds Lottie Moon sharing her adventures with three of her favorite MKs. Rachel was twelve; Edith, ten; and young Marion, eight. Lottie Moon loved to say that the missionary children of north China kept her young. The Newton girls had many "aunts" in the mission family. However, they declared their beloved "Aunt Lottie" was their number one favorite. Maybe she will be yours too!

Acknowledgments

People who write down their memories and thoughts are a blessing to those who come after them. They give us a window into history. This narrative about Lottie Moon's amazing life is possible because of the exhaustive and thorough research of historian Dr. Catherine B. Allen. She spent many years doing massive research to bring together a multitude of sources of information about Lottie Moon. Her extensive research resulted in the definitive biography of Lottie Moon's life: *The New Lottie Moon Story.*

In the forefront of all the sources was Lottie Moon herself, who wrote literally thousands of letters. Because of her diligence, we have a wonderful legacy of information about her life and work. Catherine Allen has made the heart of Lottie Moon accessible to Baptists who know and love their missions legacy.

Another who loves and preserves Baptist missions history is Kyndal Owens, records management specialist at the International Mission Board. She has been the source of countless letters, documents, pictures, and records of Lottie Moon's many years in China. She also provided pictures and information about the Newton family.

Cindy Goodwin, volunteer archivist at national Woman's Missionary Union in Birmingham, Alabama, has assisted with numerous files and documents from WMU archives.

Heather Keller, national WMU Missions Consultant for children and students, has been a terrific team member with ideas and expertise related to the ministries of Girls in Action, Royal Ambassadors, and Children in Action.

Special thanks also go to Kenny and Patsy Littleton of Guntersville,

Alabama, who have helped make possible the publication of several of these books related to sharing Baptist missions history.

Rachel Newton, the oldest of the MKs in Lottie's story, has a number of grandchildren. Her grandson, Levering Evans of Florida, has been a contributor of much-appreciated family information.

I am also especially grateful for the Courier Publishing team of Butch Blume and Denise Huffman. They have been wonderful to work with and consistently encouraging.

This book could never have seen the light of day without the editing skills of Ella Robinson. She worked many years editing for national WMU and has edited books for me since 2011. They would not be possible without her expertise and attention to detail.

Nor could these books be complete without the artwork and picture magic of our grandson, Eric Hudiburg. He has designed the covers of all six of the most recent books and edited the photos as well.

New and welcome assistance comes to this endeavor with the artwork of our daughter-in-law, Lori Hunt. This is a family project, and I am so grateful for their expertise and patience with the writer.

LOTTIE MOON
and the
SILENT BELL

Map of Shantung (Shandong) *Province*

CHAPTER ONE

LOTTIE THE COOKIE LADY

Sitting at Miss Lottie Moon's feet, eight-year-old Marion Newton wanted to know, "Aunt Lottie, why do you keep your feet on this little footstool?"

Her elderly friend smiled into the earnest young face and answered, "Because I'm so short, you see. Without my stool, these old feet of mine would just dangle in the air."

Marion nodded in understanding; she was only eight years old, and her feet always dangled from a chair when she was sitting. However, she was already nearly as tall as Miss Moon, her favorite missionary "aunt."

3

Marion realized that she would keep growing, but her Aunt Lottie was a full-grown lady and would never get any taller.

Lottie Moon was the oldest missionary that Marion and her sisters, Rachel and Edith, knew — but she was also the shortest and the liveliest. Marion was a bright young MK (missionaries' kid) and was always full of questions. One of the best times of year for the three missionary children from Hwangshien (*Hwahng She Ann*) was when they were invited to Aunt Lottie's for a visit. January in north China was bitterly cold, but, inside Miss Moon's house at Little Crossroads, her fireplace kept things nice and cozy.

Truth be told, Lottie adored visits from her young MK friends and doted on them. In turn, they loved to hear stories of her exploits as a little girl in America so many years ago. Not only that, but when Lottie told tales about her early years in China, way back in the last century, it felt like they were hearing once-upon-a-time fairy tales. Nonetheless, Miss Moon's stories were always true, and that was what made them even *more* amazing.

"Aunt Lottie," twelve-year-old Rachel, the oldest of the three sisters, held up the cookie in her hand and asked another question, "are these delicious tea cakes you always make for us the reason people call you 'The Cookie Lady'?"

Miss Moon nodded and smiled broadly at her three young guests as she explained, "You see, it all started when I first came to China way back in 1873. Let's see," and Lottie paused to try to recall the time, "that was thirty-nine years ago! I was truly eager to tell the people all around here that God loved them and sent his Son Jesus to give them eternal life. But," she stopped again and cocked her head to one side and shook it back and forth a bit, "I couldn't speak their language. How could I *tell* them?"

Ten-year-old Edith looked puzzled as she remarked, "But, Aunt

Lottie, Chinese is easy. We have spoken it ever since we started talking!"

Lottie arched her eyebrows and nodded her head a bit, "And you speak perfect Chinese, Edith. You were born here in China, and you have heard it all your life. That makes it easy for you. But," she explained, "I grew up on a plantation in Virginia, about ten thousand miles from China. I never got to hear Chinese back then. My first job when I arrived here in Tengzhou (*Duhng Joe*) was to learn this language."

Marion spoke up again, "Aunt Lottie, you sound just like a Chinese lady now."

Nodding her head in agreement, Lottie replied, "That is so, Marion. I have been living here all these many years. Day in and day out, I speak and hear Chinese. China is my *home* now." Then she smiled into each of the three young faces and added, "But I still love to speak the language of my youth, and when you girls come to visit me, I get to use English."

Rachel piped up, "Aunt Lottie, I was born in America just like you, but Mama and Daddy came to China when I was just a year old. I don't remember a *thing* about America. But all of us want to know. Where did your 'cookie lady' nickname come from?"

Drawing a nostalgic breath and making herself a bit more comfortable in her cushioned chair, Lottie explained, "Cookies became my icebreaker."

The Newton sisters looked puzzled, and Rachel asked the question on all three of their minds, "What's an icebreaker?"

Lottie Moon loved eager young minds. She explained, "You know the ice houses here in China where big chunks of ice are stored underground in the winter and then used in the summer?" Three heads nodded in agreement and Lottie continued, "Well, when your parents buy some of that ice, like when you make a freezer of delicious ice cream, you have to break up the ice into little pieces so it can be put in the ice cream churn." Of course, the girls understood that; they loved watching ice cream being churned for very special summer treats.

"Wait, Aunt Lottie," Marion sounded doubtful. "What does that have to do with cookies?"

Lottie explained, "You see, when I first came to China all those years ago, I didn't know *anything* about the Chinese language or how the people here lived and worked. I came to help them, but I couldn't even talk to them!"

Taking a deep breath, Miss Moon continued, "First of all, I had to learn their language. But do you know what?" she asked, and all three chorused, "What?" Lottie laughed, "I LOVE learning languages, that's what — and this was a new challenge!"

As usual, Marion was curious. "Aunt Lottie, tell us what all languages you can speak. Mama told us you can speak more languages than *any* of the other missionaries." Marion looked impressed.

"Well," Miss Moon narrowed her eyes and looked to one side as she pondered, "Maybe French is my favorite. It is such a beautiful, musical language. But I liked studying Latin and Italian, and," she smiled, "I certainly like Greek and Hebrew. They help me so much when I read my Bible in English and then read the same verses in Greek as well. Sometimes," she continued, "when I do my devotional reading, I like to read from my Greek New Testament." She smiled, "It makes me feel so close to Jesus, to think that He spoke that same language when He walked the earth."

All three girls were amazed that one little lady could speak and understand so many languages. Rachel asked Lottie to please read aloud in Greek her favorite verse, John 3:16. Then, at Miss Moon's request, the girls quoted it from memory in English.

Lottie's eyes twinkled as she recalled beginning to speak Chinese. She told her young friends, "I learned right away what the little children were saying as I walked down the streets or went to church. They would point their fingers at me and yell, '*Yahng gway dzuhs lie! Yahng gway dzuhs lie!*'" She gave a little laugh and translated, "I quickly learned those words meant: 'Here comes the foreign devil lady!' I wanted so badly to tell them that I had come to China to tell them that Jesus loved them, so I studied as hard and as quickly as I could."

"But then," Lottie stopped, and, as was her habit, cocked her head to one side, "I had to find a way to get to *know* them. I couldn't just walk up to a house, knock on the door and say, 'I want to tell you about God and His love.' How could I get to *know* them and get them to want to listen? So," she explained to her young friends who were wondering what happened next, "I decided to try an icebreaker. I had to break that big chunk of 'ice' that separated me from all the people around me. I needed something that would allow me to get to know each of the children."

Miss Moon gave a big smile and clapped her hands, "And then, I remembered my Virginia recipe for tea cakes! The children would walk by my little house here at Little Crossroads, and they could smell the delicious fragrance of baking cookies."

Marion spoke up, "Like these cookies we are eating, Aunt Lottie?"

"Exactly," their friend replied, "the little ones loved those cookies, and they would tell their friends about them. Even *more* children would come! That's the way I got those closed doors to open up."

Rachel grinned and asked her, "Did they still call you 'foreign devil'?"

Lottie chuckled, "No more, Rachel. I started a school and began teaching them how to read and write. Before you know it, they were calling me '*Tyan Shoo Kuh*,' the Heavenly Book Visitor. I liked that. Isn't that what all missionaries are?"

Rachel had a question. "Aunt Lottie, I have always wondered how it was that you came to China so long ago, and you came all by yourself." Rachel sounded amazed at the thought of someone being that brave.

As usual, Marion added a question, "Weren't you *scared*, Aunt Lottie, to come all that way alone?" Marion sounded in awe of her intrepid elderly friend. "I would have been so scared!" She gave a little shudder at the thought.

Miss Moon smiled gently as she admitted, "Marion, I was a wee bit apprehensive. But," she concluded, "I wasn't really by myself. I knew the dear Lord who wanted me to come here and tell the good news about Jesus. I knew He was coming with me to China."

Rachel had yet another request. "Please, won't you tell us what it was like growing up in America? I have been so curious. All I know about that country is what I read, and what Mama and Daddy tell me." Rachel shook her head in wonderment, "Here I am an American, but I really am a stranger to my own country!"

Lottie nodded in understanding, "Rachel, I do know that feeling, and I admit to you, after thirty-nine years of living in China, it is now *America* that seems like a foreign land to me!"

Edith, who had been listening closely but asking little, spoke up, "Well, I was born in China, so I don't know *anything* about America, and I wish I did. Will you please tell us, Aunt Lottie, what it was like being a little girl in America? Did you have a big family?" Edith grinned and added what all of them knew, "We have a big family, you know!" A home with nine children certainly qualified as large.

Lottie Moon gave a laugh and added, "Girls, you have bested me! My family only had seven children." Everyone chuckled together.

Lottie looked at her little lapel watch and added, "I would love to tell you tales of growing up in America, but look," and she pointed at the watch on her lapel, "it's growing quite late. Let's plan to have our 'once upon a time in America' stories tomorrow evening."

"Fun!" Marion agreed, and happily led the way to their bedroom.

At the door of the girls' room, Lottie reached out and kissed each tender cheek, softly saying, "I am so glad you girls have come to visit. God bless and keep you, my young friends. Until tomorrow."

The Rest of the Story

Lottie Moon became a legend in her own time among the younger missionaries who joined in the work in north China. Furthermore, the numerous MKs (missionaries' kids) who lived in the whole area loved her dearly and never forgot how she loved them in return. Lottie vowed that those children kept her young at heart. Having them come for a visit made her feel like part of their families and made up for much of the loneliness she experienced when living alone for months at a time in the interior. For long periods, she never saw another foreigner or heard anyone speak English. Showing hospitality was something that her Virginia family had always loved to do. All her years in China, Lottie thrived on opportunities to welcome visitors, both Chinese and foreign. Her famous cookies were a special part of that expression of caring for others.

Extra Credit

Make a batch of cookies using Lottie's own recipe. Share it with an elderly friend who cannot easily get out and visit. When you share your baking, tell your friend about "The Cookie Lady," Miss Lottie Moon. Maybe your elderly friend will have some stories to share with you.

Miss Lottie's Cookie Recipe

2 cups flour   1 well-beaten egg

¼ cup butter   1 Tablespoon cream

1 heaping cup sugar

Preheat oven to 425 degrees F. Cream butter and sugar. Add egg and mix well. Add flour and cream. Dust a board with flour and a little sugar. Roll the dough very thin. Cut cookies with a water glass or a round cookie cutter. Place on greased cookie sheet. Bake for about five minutes. Remove and cool on a rack.

Lottie Moon's signatures. One on the left: from her calling card, pronounced Li Tea Aw *(transliteration of Lottie). One on the right: her surname* Moo, *followed by* Lah Tee, *translated "Moon Lottie."*

C̄HA PT̄ER T̄WO

LOTTIE AND THE SILENT BELL

Lottie Moon and her three young guests were finishing their evening meal when Rachel spoke, "Aunt Lottie, we've all finished." She was a dignified twelve now and the oldest of all the Newton children, but she was as excited as Marion and Edith about hearing Aunt Lottie tell stories from her childhood in America. Nobody could tell tales quite like Aunt Lottie.

Miss Moon smiled as she carefully folded her napkin and neatly returned it to the napkin ring beside her plate. "Well, my young friends," she smiled one by one into each pair of eager eyes, "so you are ready right now for our story time?" A chorus of "Yes-es" rang out, and all four trooped to the sitting room. Lottie sat in her favorite chair and rested her small feet on her handy footstool.

"Let's begin with our favorite opening, all right?" Lottie began. Three heads nodded as Lottie settled back into her chair.

"Once upon a time," and she gave a dramatic pause before adding, "and it was a *loooong* time ago, a little girl was born in faraway America in Virginia. That little girl was *indeed* little, for she never grew even as tall as you already are, Edith," she said, nodding her head in the direction of ten-year-old Edith. "I know there are nine children in your family," Lottie noted, "and there were seven children in *my* family. Well, that little girl in Virginia that I'm talking about was me. I was the middle child of seven."

All three Newton girls grinned and nodded. They had known all along Aunt Lottie was talking about herself. They also knew what it felt like to live in a large family.

"Girls," Lottie began, "I lived on a large plantation. We had a lot of land and many places to romp and play. In fact, Viewmont (that is what we called our home) had more than 1,500 acres of land," she confided. "Our house was large enough to hold fifteen beds, and would you believe," she smiled, "sometimes all of those beds were filled with cousins and aunts and uncles and a houseful of noise! I was shorter than anybody else, but my boy cousins learned right away it might not be a good idea to pick on me. My mouth wasn't little. I could make a lot of noise and hold my own in an argument. I remember," Lottie stopped and gazed into the distance, as if recalling those days of long ago, "that some of my aunts and uncles liked to disagree with each other, and fuss about what we ought to believe about the Bible and about different churches. I got so tired of all the fussing and bickering that I decided in my heart that I didn't need any of that religion business."

Lottie confessed, "I must admit to you, I thought I was pretty intelligent. I really didn't need God in my life. I was fine just like I was!"

The Newton girls looked a bit shocked, and Rachel spoke up, "Aunt Lottie, that doesn't sound like you!"

Lottie agreed, "You are so right, Rachel. I had a lot of growing up to do. To tell the truth, I didn't *like* to go to church. You had to sit there so long, and the preacher would talk on and on and on. Our benches at church had prickly horsehair cushions. After an hour or so, those cushions were most uncomfortable!" Three young heads nodded in agreement. They knew how hard it was to sit still for a long time. It often happened to them as well.

Then Lottie recalled another vivid memory and chuckled as she told the Newton girls about an unforgettable Sunday dinner. The children listened intently as Lottie related that long-ago tale. "One Sunday morning, I regret to admit, I played hooky from church."

Three young faces glanced at one another with questioning expressions, as if to say, "Surely not Auntie Lottie!"

"I told Mama that I didn't feel good; my head hurt. Mama sounded worried, but she asked me to just rest and stay quiet. Surely, I would feel better soon. Well," and Lottie gave a little grin, "I only stayed still 'til the carriage pulled out onto the main road. You see, Mama didn't believe in doing *anything* like work on Sunday. All our servants had the day off so they could worship too. Our kitchen was in a separate building in those days, because of the danger of fire. The kitchen door was carefully locked, so I crawled in through a window. It took a lot of work, but I whipped up quite a nice Sunday dinner. All the time I was thinking that Mama wouldn't be too angry, because I had prepared a good hot meal."

Lottie raised both black eyebrows and cocked her head to one side. Looking a bit like a mischievous little sparrow, she drew in a deep breath, "Well, Mama was NOT amused. I promise you I never pulled that kind of stunt again!" Chuckling again, she added, "I must tell you though, I had so much fun cooking!"

Lottie shifted in her chair and began to tell the Newton girls about a very important part of her childhood. "I didn't go to school," Lottie declared. "We had a governess, and she could speak very beautiful French." Lottie smiled, "It became my favorite language, although I was able to learn six other languages through the years. And, of course," Lottie added, "Chinese is now the language of my heart." She patted her heart, as if emphasizing just how much she loved Chinese. "When I was a young girl, I especially loved reading and writing. It was my favorite time of day when I could let my imagination wander and write stories and compositions to my heart's content!"

"Aunt Lottie," Rachel wondered, "did you go to college?"

"Oh yes, dear girl, and I loved every minute of it, even the exams. When I was nearly fourteen, Mama sent me to Hollins Institute (now Hollins University) near Roanoke, and I studied there for two years. They used to call Hollins a finishing school. I loved studying languages and English, especially Latin and French. However," and again the twinkle in Lottie's eyes was very evident, "I thought life on campus was a bit dull and boring. One day I decided to do something about it." All three girls leaned forward, eager to hear what the dignified and scholarly Miss Moon did to liven things up.

Miss Moon's eyes held that mischievous little sparkle as she explained, "That was back in 1855, and I was all of fourteen years old. It was March 31, and the next day was April Fool's Day. What better time to have some fun?" A look of anticipation lighted up each face as the girls listened intently. "I got up before daylight and gathered up all my extra bed sheets. A large bell hung in a tower on campus. Our days began with the ringing of that bell, calling for everyone to get up and prepare for the day." Lottie's own face was alight with glee as she recalled,

"I quietly crept up the tower steps just as dawn was beginning to break. I carefully muffled the bell with all those sheets," Lottie chuckled. "Well, everything started late that day, from breakfast to classes and everything all day long. Of course," she finished, "it was easy for the faculty to figure out who the sheets belonged to. I was severely scolded, and my report card that spring was marked 'Highly Deficient' in deportment (that means behavior)!"

"However, ladies," Lottie addressed her young guests, "I finally grew up. After Hollins, I went to a brand-new college for girls in Charlottesville, Virginia. Some educators had decided that women could learn just like men could. And they were right," she added. "I loved learning, and I absorbed all I could. I didn't love rules, though, and I certainly didn't like to go to church. All my friends, especially my best friend, Julia Toy, were sincerely worried because I was outspoken about being a skeptic. Do you girls know what 'skeptic' means?" and she looked at Rachel.

Rachel responded, "I think it means to be a doubter."

"You are exactly right, dear girl," Lottie nodded her head. "I honestly didn't think I needed God. I was fine just like I was. Well," she nodded her head as she recalled that time so long ago, "the church right next to campus was having a revival meeting. Dr. John Broadus, a very well-known Baptist minister and professor, was leading the services each night. I must confess to you, I decided to go to the service that night just to make fun of all that religion stuff." The girls looked a little startled to hear their wonderful Aunt Lottie say such a thing.

"But," Lottie paused and drew in her breath, "I went back to my room to pray all night. You see, it began with a barking dog. I didn't want to think about what Dr. Broadus had talked about. I didn't want to think about my very soul being in peril. Lost? I was lost? I would not go to heaven?" Lottie recalled. "I certainly didn't want to think about that. I tried and tried to go to sleep, but that silly old dog that lived next to our dormitory just wouldn't quit barking. On and on and on. And, as that dog barked, I began to think about the condition of my eternal soul." Lottie's eyes glazed over as she stared into space, remembering that very moment so long ago.

"Girls," she sighed, "I started that night thinking I didn't need God at all, and I ended up giving my heart to Christ. And then," a beautiful smile marked the memory of that experience, "and *then*, my life completely turned around. From being a skeptic, I became a follower. You see the result," she concluded. "I followed Christ's call all the way to China! The rest is history. Oh my, the amazing adventures I have had these many years. You could say," she finished with a smile, "it all began with a barking dog!"

"Aunt Lottie," Rachel clearly had more questions, "how did you know this was what God wanted for you?" Rachel's face showed her puzzlement. "It is a long distance from a college in America to coming all alone to China. That is halfway around the world."

Marion broke in, "Aunt Lottie, you did that all by yourself? That must have been extremely scary. Mama didn't have to come by herself, 'cause she had Daddy."

"Well, dear child," Lottie nodded at Marion's observation, "I'm not going to say that I didn't have a few moments of wondering what in the world I was about to do. I had quite a lot of unanswered questions." Miss Moon stopped and again seemed to be thinking of some long-ago memory. Drawing in a long breath, she spoke, "However, something happened in America that changed life for everyone in the United States. For more than four years, we had a huge, long, deadly war in America. My home country changed in so many ways. A number of years passed before I could set sail for China. And then, what an adventure life became!"

All three girls' faces looked eagerly at Miss Moon. Edith, usually the quiet sister, impulsively requested, "Aunt Lottie, tell us about that terrible war and what happened to you."

Miss Moon slowly nodded her head a time or so, then reminded her young audience, "Oh my, we can't stay up that late. That war was like another whole once-upon-a-time story of its own. That tale has some buried treasure in it too. How about saving it for tomorrow?"

Having something to look forward to suited the three Newton sisters. Everyone headed off to bed, eagerly looking forward to story time the next evening.

The Rest of the Story

Shortly after Lottie Moon's graduation from college, civil war tore through the United States of America with bloodshed and sorrow. That war forever changed the United States. Lottie, like everyone else in the country, was affected by the pain and conflict of war between brother and brother, sister and sister. However, Lottie Moon did not let those changes keep her from following God's purpose for her life. Little did she know that God would use her far beyond the land of China. Her life and heroism impacted an entire denomination for the many years ahead. Lottie never set out to be a hero — just to tell the good news of God's great love to a perishing people who had never heard. That ended up being the very thing she accomplished. God also used her to influence millions of believers in America, inspiring them to support missions through giving, praying, and even going to the mission field.

Extra Credit

Go online to explore the history of Hollins University in Virginia, and/or the way Albemarle Female Seminary was founded. You might want to explore Catherine Allen's book *The New Lottie Moon Story* and learn about the outstanding reputation the young Lottie Moon had as a scholar and writer. Allen's book may be in your church library or found on Amazon.com or Bookfinder.com.

Sketch of Lottie and the muffled bell (By Lori Windsor Hunt)

CHAPTER THREE

LOTTIE AND THE BURIED TREASURE

Three happy children with buried treasure on their minds did not linger over supper the following evening, so eager they were to hear about Aunt Lottie's Civil War adventure. Rachel was already thinking about how excited her little brothers and sisters would be when she got home and told them about real treasure being buried.

As the girls arranged themselves on the little rug by Aunt Lottie's chair, Marion's face revealed her excitement. "We're ready to hear about the buried treasure, Aunt Lottie. I've been wondering about it all day!"

Miss Moon's eyes twinkled, and she raised her eyebrows as she explained, "Of course, Miss Marion, but I must first tell you how I got from college days and through a war and then to buried treasure. You see, I am the one who did the burying.

"Once upon a time," again, Lottie began with their favorite opening line, "a young college graduate went home after completing her studies, all eager to get started on the rest of her life. Of course, I was that young graduate, and I was excited to have gotten not just a college degree, but also an advanced one called a master's degree. Most women were not encouraged to pursue advanced degrees back then, but several of the leading men in our Baptist convention were convinced that women were as intelligent as men. They believed we deserved a chance to learn just like our brothers did. So, they started this college for women."

Three heads nodded in agreement; they certainly believed that they had good minds like their brothers did.

"Just then, however," Miss Moon's eyes clouded over, "war began in America, and brothers fought against brothers. As the Civil War started, the clanging of swords and the sounds of gunfire could be heard in many states. Some of the fighting was scarily close to our home in Virginia. My brothers, my cousins, and my uncles and friends all marched off to battle. We women were left at home to take care of all the work. We had to protect our homes and property too," Lottie sighed. Her eyes seemed to be seeing again the frightening and tragic happenings of those years. "We saw wounded soldiers and hurting people. It was as if our whole world had been turned upside down.

"And truly," she shook her head in sorrow, "our world *was* upside down. Life as I had always known it was gone forever. I clearly recall the time in 1865, when General Robert E. Lee surrendered to the Union troops. Right after that, rumors started that Union soldiers were filling our countryside. Everyone was in a panic, including all of us at Viewmont. A town nearby went up in flames of battle, and now we were doubly frightened. What if the enemy soldiers came to Viewmont? How could we protect ourselves? All the men with guns and swords were away from home fighting. There was no one to help us."

Lottie leaned forward in her chair, "I must explain to you that Mother was a very brave woman. She was not young or strong, but she had a strong heart and a lot of determination. She called all of us to prayer and to action. We learned that the enemy was nearby. Time was most important. We had to protect our treasures as best we could. All of us piled food and clothing onto a wagon and one of the plantation helpers drove the wagon about twenty miles away, deep in the woods of Viewmont. Somehow, we had to keep those basics for living out of the enemy's hands."

Lottie paused and took off her glasses to rub her weary eyes. As she replaced them, she recalled, "I confess, I was scared — but I knew I had to be strong for Mama's sake. She gathered up all the family silver and jewels and thrust them into my hands. My hands were shaking so badly." Lottie lifted her shaking hands to illustrate. "I thought I was going to drop some of the treasure. This was jewelry that had been handed down in our family for generations. Here it was in my small and weak hands. I didn't waste any time, though. I piled the jewels and silverware into boxes and headed to the orchard to bury them."

Miss Moon's face took on a resigned look as she remembered that scary day. "I did just what Mama asked. I buried that silver and all those jewels in the orchard and hurried back home to wait for the enemy. Would you believe," and she paused as three young women leaned forward to hear what happened next, "the enemy never came to Viewmont! We waited and waited and waited some more — nothing. The enemy simply bypassed our place. Thank God. The next day, the family wagon safely returned with our food and clothing."

"But what about the buried treasure?" asked Rachel.

Lottie sighed deeply. "It was never found. Evidently, I had been so frightened that I simply could not remember just where I had buried that treasure. All the trees looked alike that spring. We dug and we dug, one spot after another, and the treasure was *never* discovered."

The girls looked as regretful as did Miss Moon at the memory. Then Lottie smiled, "However, about ten years ago, I got a letter from one of my sisters. Some farmers were plowing in the place where our orchard had been. Their plows turned up several pieces of jewelry. A bit of our buried treasure had really been found again!"

Lottie moved on to another war story, "Girls, would you like another little tidbit of wartime adventure?"

Three heads nodded at the same time. "Oh yes!" exclaimed Marion. She never got tired of exciting stories.

"Well," Lottie began, "evidently one Charlotte Moon is not enough." The MKs looked puzzled until she continued. "I had a first cousin who, like me, was named for our grandmother, Charlotte Moon. Also like me, she was nicknamed 'Lottie.' She and her family lived in Ohio. My cousin Lottie was a feisty prankster and had a streak of raw courage."

Lottie chuckled when she noticed the look on Rachel's face, "I see you think I was a prankster too, don't you?" Rachel grinned sheepishly and nodded.

"Maybe so," Lottie admitted, "but in the 1860s, Cousin Lottie had many daring adventures as a spy for the Confederacy. Just before the war started, she was engaged to marry a fellow called Ambrose Burnside. The wedding day came, and Lottie walked down the aisle to stand by her husband-to-be. The minister solemnly began the service. But when he got to the part that said, 'Lottie, do you take Ambrose to be your lawfully wedded husband?' Cousin Lottie spoke up, 'No sir, I don't!' The whole congregation sat there in shock."

Lottie concluded, "Well, the War Between the States (that's another name for the Civil War) started, and Cousin Lottie became a spy for the Confederacy. As fortune would have it, Mr. Burnside, the man she had almost married, became a high officer in the Union army! One day," Lottie kept the girls in suspense for long moments, "Union soldiers caught Cousin Lottie spying and arrested her. They quickly took their prisoner to appear before their general. Of all people, it was General Ambrose Burnside!" Lottie shook her head back and forth and chuckled. "Happily, General Burnside was a chivalrous gentleman and didn't hold a grudge against the young woman who had jilted him at the altar. He soon released her from custody."

The girls heaved a sigh of satisfaction at hearing how the tale ended. And Lottie grinned, "I told you she was feisty!"

"That terrible war finally ended," Lottie concluded the tale. "I was thankful for my good education. All through the war years, I was able to tutor students to make money and help my family through the hard times. I did private tutoring for several families, some of them in Georgia and some in South Carolina."

Lottie chuckled as she remembered one of her students. "Girls, I'll not forget young Percy who lived in South Carolina. His father, Mr. Middlebrooks, was a wealthy Baptist deacon, and he wanted his bright young son to be highly educated. Mr. Middlebrooks was delighted to employ me to tutor his son. When I agreed to the job, I asked that they allow me two free hours each afternoon for my own time. That way, I could read and meditate and study the Bible.

"Mind you," Lottie laughed, "young Mr. Percy was pretty clever. One afternoon, a gaggle of geese came from the barn to settle down right under my window. You've never heard such squawking and noise! So, I gave Percy five cents to drive them away. Would you believe, those pesky geese began coming every afternoon to settle under my window. Well," and Lottie nodded her head, "I soon realized why. Intrepid little Mr. Percy *arranged* for those geese to be under my window *every* afternoon." Lottie gave a little laugh, "However, it was worth a nickel a day to have peace and quiet!"

Moving ahead with her tales, Lottie explained, "After the war was over and peace secured, I needed more steady work to help our family. Our plantation was no longer producing crops and money. My first large job was teaching in Danville, Kentucky, at a girls' school opened by the First Baptist Church there. The school offered free tuition to daughters of Baptist ministers whose families had been hit hard by the war.

"I loved teaching those young women. But let me tell you, girls," and three sets of ears leaned forward to hear Aunt Lottie's words, "at that same time, a medical missionary to China, Dr. G.W. Burton, came to Danville to my church. I began learning so much about China. I loved hearing Dr. Burton tell about his experiences when he lived there. I realized that God was using that quiet and gentle man to write China on my heart."

Lottie shifted in her chair, "But of course, what could I do? I was a young woman. Back then, the Foreign Mission Board would not appoint single women as missionaries. They had appointed one years before, and evidently it did not work out. So, they didn't appoint any more. Then, the Civil War started, and our board could scarcely pay the salaries of its missionaries already serving. So, I prayed. I taught school. I asked God to guide me, for I wanted to be His servant wherever He wanted me."

"Did you stay in Kentucky, Aunt Lottie?" Rachel wanted to know.

Lottie shook her head, "No. I was asked to go with a teacher friend to Cartersville, Georgia, to begin a select academy for girls. I loved the challenge of starting something new. My friend and I had wonderful students who were eager to learn. Those two years in Georgia were so busy. I also learned some handy skills about how to start a school.

But China was ever on my mind. I kept corresponding with Dr. Henry Tupper in Richmond, Virginia. By the way, do any of you know who he was?" she inquired.

Rachel spoke up, "Mama told me Dr. Tupper used to be the president of the Foreign Mission Board."

Lottie smiled and nodded. "That's right. I often wrote him about going to China. I did this for more than two years because I could never get China off my heart. At the very same time, my pastor in Cartersville also had missions on *his* mind. I'll never forget the Sunday morning he preached about the needs of the world to know God's love. His words spoke right to me."

Lottie frowned a little, "But I was frustrated, because, of course, our mission board would not appoint single women. I was not married, so I had a problem." Miss Moon glanced at her little lapel watch and shook her head, "Oh dear, we have a little problem right now. It's getting late. We'll have to learn the solution to the China dilemma tomorrow!"

Three young voices protested, "Oh, we have to wait again?"

Their Aunt Lottie smiled as they all headed to bed. "Tomorrow is just a few hours away!"

The Rest of the Story

In this century, women can go into missions service either as a wife or a single woman. Through her persistence, even though Lottie Moon was not married, she was appointed as a Southern Baptist missionary in 1873. Up until that time, appointing single women was a big issue and one that was frequently debated. Lottie Moon ended up blazing such a trail that her name has been deeply carved into the history of Baptist missions. She was genuinely loved by the believers in north China, and no one was more respected among missionaries than the renowned Lottie Moon. She was a master letter writer. Her hundreds and thousands of letters mailed back to America inspired Baptists across the United States to support missions, pray for missionaries, and, often, to go and serve themselves. God used Lottie Moon's life of sacrifice and service as inspiration for an entire denomination.

Extra Credit

Secure a copy of Catherine Allen's *The New Lottie Moon Story* and learn interesting details about the beginning of appointing single women for missions service. Lottie was indeed a trail blazer. You will also find fascinating stories in Allen's book about Lottie and her family during the Civil War. You can learn still more about pioneer work she began in the interior, going where people had never before seen a foreigner.

A sample of Lottie Moon's letter writing (Photo courtesy of International Mission Board)

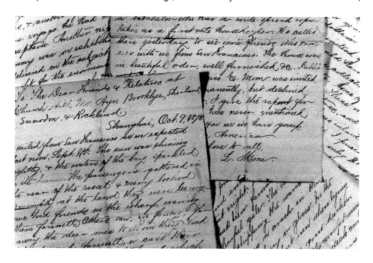

Monument Street Church, Tengzhou (Photo courtesy of International Mission Board)

CHAPTER FOUR

LOTTIE SETS SAIL

"You must have come to China long before our mama and daddy did, Aunt Lottie," Rachel commented that cold winter evening as everyone settled into their favorite spots for story time.

"Oh, yes," Miss Moon agreed, "and the trip to get here was one I'll never forget. Before that happened, though, I was so excited when I learned that our Baptist board had *finally* agreed to appoint single women." She smiled at her young guests as she recalled that exciting day in 1873.

"Girls, on September 1, I was appointed as a missionary, and you would have thought I had been given a bag of gold. To me, it was just as valuable as gold; at long last I was going where I felt God wanted me to be. I admit to you," and Lottie's face looked serious, "it was exciting, but it was also sad at the same time."

The girls seemed puzzled, so Lottie explained, "I had to say goodbye to all my family. I did not think I would ever be able to see them again."

Rachel interrupted, "But why, Aunt Lottie? You would have a furlough in about seven years and could visit America again."

Lottie shook her head, "No, my child. In those early days, there was no such thing as a furlough. When you sailed away from home, you knew you would never be back. Our board provided no means for us to go home to see our families." Lottie hastened to add, "I'll tell you later how furloughs came to be. Right now, though, let me explain how I got to China."

With a question in her voice, Marion impulsively asked, "Aunt Lottie, were you a little bit scared? Mama told us that you are the bravest lady she has ever known, and I believe it." Her eyes looked wide at the thought. "You came all those thousands of miles across the Pacific Ocean all by yourself." She shook her head in disbelief, "I would have been so scared to come without my daddy or my mama … or a husband."

Lottie chuckled and raising her eyebrows, nodding, "Don't think me brave, girls. It is just that in my heart I *knew* that I wasn't alone. I never doubted that God was with me all the way."

The sisters settled in for the next tale as Lottie told of her long journey. She first went to Alabama where her sister Orie (Orianna) lived. Orie and William, her husband, were both doctors, and they gave Lottie some important training in how to help sick people. Lottie knew that there were very few doctors in China, so she figured she needed to develop some doctoring skills. Lottie sighed as she told the girls, "After

I said goodbye to my oldest sister, I sadly boarded a train to go to San Francisco. That long overland trip proved to be the hardest part of the whole journey. I traveled from Alabama to New York and then all the way across America to San Francisco. It took two whole weeks."

Lottie smiled as she recalled, "It was a beautiful, crisp September morning when I boarded our ship, the SS *Costa Rica,* in San Francisco. The sun was sparkling on the water in the harbor, and it felt like I was sailing off into a whole new life." Lottie stopped, then nodded her head, "And it *was* a whole new life. It was full of trouble and trial and tragedy and tedium — but most of all, it was full of joy. I knew I was where God wanted me to be." Lottie patted her heart and finished, "And that was the greatest feeling of all."

"Was it fun to sail on a big ship, Aunt Lottie?" Edith asked.

"Yes and no," Lottie smiled. "It was fun to get on board and meet other missionaries headed to Japan and China. The fun stopped quickly, though. Our first night out at sea was miserable. It was my stomach!" She put her hand over her stomach, and shook her head back and forth, recalling those miserable days on a tossing sea.

"I was sick the whole trip and could scarcely stand up and move. When we anchored in Tokyo harbor in Japan, I literally wept for joy at seeing land again. The ground didn't roll around me all the time like the ocean water had. We had a few hours in Tokyo, and I loved riding in a rickshaw and seeing that beautiful city," she told the attentive girls. "Of course, when we got back on the ship, the seasickness came right back! But," she added, "it was worth it to finally get to China. This would be my new home. I was so excited to see it for the first time," Lottie smiled as she remembered those feelings that swept over her that first week nearly four decades earlier.

"Our harbor in Chefoo was beautiful. All of you have been to Chefoo, haven't you?" Lottie asked. The girls nodded a quick "yes."

Lottie reminded them that it was over ninety miles from that harbor city to Tengzhou. "I traveled those long ninety miles in a *shendz (shun dzzz)*." The girls gave a collective little groan. A *shendz* was a kind of cart with a padded chair on it where a passenger could sit. This was attached to poles and pulled by mules, one in front and one behind, with a driver walking along leading them. The passenger sitting in the *shendz* felt every bump in the road. Lottie laughed at the memory. "It felt like a ninety-mile torture chamber!"

"I was so relieved when we finally arrived. I felt like I had been bumping along in that *shendz* for at least three weeks instead of three days!" Lottie recalled, "There were about five Baptist missionaries living here then, and the same number of Presbyterians. All of them gave me a royal welcome. My heart was so happy because I was finally here.

"I realize everything here in China looks natural to you girls," Lottie continued, "because you have seen it all your lives. But I had never seen anything like this before." Shaking her head in wonder, Lottie thought back, "Can you imagine how all the new sights, the sounds, the smells hit me?" she asked her small audience. "Everything looked different. It sounded different — and, oh my, did it smell and *taste* different!"

She explained, "I became handy with chopsticks right away, but my stomach never really adjusted to what those chopsticks picked up!" Lottie gave a little shudder, and the Newton girls giggled. "Of course, I loved rice," she explained. "I grew up eating rice in Virginia. But, oh my goodness, when missionaries took me to visit in homes here, the strange food they served me was a shock." Lottie lifted one finger, then another, as if counting off those strange foods. "It was all so different. There were pickled jelly fish and field eel that seemed to swim around in oil. Then there were fried grasshoppers and lots of garlic and oil, along with plenty of sea slugs."

As the list went on, the Newton sisters began to chuckle. They had tasted some of those same things, so they knew how their Aunt Lottie felt.

"When I first arrived," Lottie went on, "I gazed at all the strange and unusual sights and heard all this strange language being spoken. I wondered how on earth I could ever make sense out of it." Noticing the look on the girls' faces, Lottie chuckled, "I know, I know. It sounds so natural to your ears. But to these foreign ears of mine, it sounded like nothing so much as a bunch of chickens clucking at each other.

"However, I was captivated by the bright faces of the children that followed me everywhere. They had sparkling eyes and shiny hair and were always laughing, especially while they pointed at me and jabbered. A new missionary friend translated for me and interpreted the questions with which they peppered me. Their favorite one," Lottie recalled, "was, 'How old are you?' Some of them even wanted to know if I was *nánde* or *nyǔde* — boy or girl. I quickly learned to make sense of some of those words they repeated over and over, and began answering them in Chinese. That delighted the youngsters, and then they would come with still more questions. I fell in love with those children."

Lottie paused and added, "I learned very soon that the Chinese language, as difficult as it sounded to my ears, was not as big a challenge as learning and accepting the Chinese culture. So much was different from how we acted and lived in America. But then," Lottie looked intently at each of the girls, "who is to say our American way of doing things is the better way? After all, people have been living and speaking and working in China long before our country even became a nation. Chinese and American cultures are just *different*.

"But," she continued, "I had not been here a week before I was overwhelmed with the thought, *I came to tell these people that God loves them, but I can't even talk to them.* That was my first order of business. After all, I love learning languages, and here was my newest challenge. It was an important one."

Lottie recalled, "One of our missionaries knew of a fine old scholar who didn't know a word of English. However, his Chinese was flawless. Mr. Wang became my teacher, and I was determined to learn all I could. I must confess," Lottie smiled confidingly, "I found all the tones a real task. I had to concentrate and listen so carefully. I found the written characters fascinating, though. I set myself a goal of learning a certain number each week."

"Aunt Lottie, we study characters each week too," Edith happily told her elderly friend. "Mama teaches us, of course, but we have two hours every week when we study Chinese vocabulary and characters with a Chinese lady. I like drawing, and writing characters is a lot like drawing a picture."

Lottie agreed, then paused a moment before saying, "Now, where was I? I must have been telling you about the new things that I experienced that first week I was in China. I wasn't prepared for all of them. Those early days were a shock. But, oh my, there was one thing that really shook me up. It disturbed me and stunned me all at the same time."

Marion's little cherub face was bright with curiosity, "What, Aunt Lottie? What was it?"

Miss Moon got that mischievous look on her face and raised her eyebrows, "Well, Miss Marion, let's find out tomorrow evening!"

All three girls gave a sigh of resignation, and Edith said, "Come on, Aunt Lottie, we need to know now!"

"I'm afraid this tale is too long for one evening. Let's check back tomorrow night," Lottie answered. With a sigh of resignation all mixed in with anticipation, the three sisters headed to bed to dream about things that might shake someone up.

The Rest of the Story

Our earliest missionaries, when going to their new countries, left America with the understanding that they would never see their families or their homeland ever again on this earth. That was one of the greatest sacrifices an early missionary had to make. Another was the difference in cultures. New missionaries often left America full of enthusiasm and excitement about following Christ's command to go into all the world and tell the good news. Then reality came: a totally new language, a culture completely unlike their own, strange customs, strange foods, and nothing familiar and comforting. Many were not prepared, and the strain was too great for scores of those who went. Lottie Moon came to quickly understand the difficulty so many of her fellow missionaries were facing. She wanted something to be done about it. Lottie became the main one who brought about a system of furloughs.

Extra Credit

What is your favorite Chinese food? Are you handy with chopsticks? With the help of your missions leader or your parents, learn how to make a simple and tasty Chinese dish. Lottie didn't care for Chinese food, but who knows? Your family might like your Chinese cooking!

Shendz (shun dzzz) – *A common form of transportation
in eighteenth and nineteenth century China (Sketch by Lori Windsor Hunt)*

Child with bound feet, 1892, Ching Dynasty, China

CHAPTER FIVE

LOTTIE STARTS A SCHOOL

It was January, and January in north China can be bitterly cold. The Newton sisters stayed indoors, intent upon school assignments. Mama had given them work to do during their visit with Aunt Lottie. Through most of the day, they kept warm near the sitting room fireplace. All three talked about what might have most shocked Miss Moon when she first came to China.

Even while studying, the three girls were already anticipating suppertime. It was a great time to chat about the day with Aunt Lottie. Li Tai Tai (*Lee Tie Tie*) had been cooking and helping Aunt Lottie for many years. She knew how to cook simple American food. When Miss Moon was out in the country teaching, she could only eat Chinese food. So, when she was home in Tengzhou (*Duhng Joe*), Lottie wanted to eat only simple American-style food. Not surprisingly, Li Tai Tai's favorite thing to bake was Miss Moon's cookies. That was the Newton girls' favorite too.

This evening's meal moved along quite rapidly, for the sisters were all eager to get to story time. In a couple of days, they would be going home. They knew that soon they would be missing their favorite time of the day with Aunt Lottie. So, they wanted as much story time as possible.

Marion skipped along, leading the way to Aunt Lottie's sitting room after supper. All three girls found their favorite spots at Aunt Lottie's knee, waiting with happy anticipation for the evening's adventure to begin. Marion started off with the question on all their minds: "Aunt Lottie, what on earth was the *biggest* shock to you? I've been trying to guess all day."

Lottie smiled and teased their curiosity a little bit more. "Well, the smells were a shock." Three heads nodded in understanding. "The masses of people were a shock." More nods. "The constant noise and busyness and all the questions people asked me were a shock. But," and she finally, added, "nothing hit me quite like the tiny bound feet of the women!" All three heads bobbed up and down. It *always* made them feel sad to see the little bound feet on girls and women.

Bound feet seemed so cruel and unnecessary to all the sisters. Rachel spoke up, "Aunt Lottie, I saw a little old lady one day, sitting on a stool in front of her house. She had a bowl of warm water for washing her feet right at her side. I could see as she took off her tiny little embroidered shoes and began unwinding the cloths that were wrapped around each foot." Rachel gave a little gulp of sympathy, saying, "My heart was wrung with pity. Her tiny feet were so deformed. I could see that all five toes had been bent under and formed into one little point. Aunt Lottie," Rachel's eyes filled with tears at the memory, "I just thanked God my mother never had to do that to my feet. Every step that lady took for the rest of her life was painful."

Lottie Moon nodded her head in understanding, "You can easily see why I was so shocked to see beautiful little girls hobbling around." Lottie shook her head in sympathy. "I had read about the custom of binding the feet of young girls, but actually *seeing* it up close struck sorrow to my heart."

Reaching out, one by one, Lottie placed a gentle hand on top of each curly-haired child and responded, "Rachel, I am thankful all of you have healthy feet. Being able to help young Chinese girls is one of the biggest joys I have here in China. Let me tell you how this came about. Think back with me, girls," Lottie suggested, "to one of our story times. Remember how they called me the 'Cookie Lady'?" All three nodded immediately.

"You recall the cookies won the children over," Lottie explained. "The cookies gave me a way to meet the children's mothers and talk with them. I got to know about their everyday lives and what mattered to them. And those mothers, every one of them, loved their little girls. *If we had a school for girls,* I thought, *we would have a way to help them learn about God's love.* Then those girls would be able to read and write and learn how God loved them. And, in turn, they could help their *own* families learn about God's love."

"But, Aunt Lottie," again Rachel spoke up, and she was frowning, "we hear that Chinese fathers don't think girls *need* to read and write."

Lottie gave a ladylike snort and nodded her head, "Too true, dear girl, so it took time and persuasion. You see, if parents agreed to let their girls attend school, we gave them free tuition, and they could stay and board at the school. That persuaded many of the fathers. And that made the girls' mothers extremely happy."

"Was it fun to start a school, Aunt Lottie?" Edith was curious.

"Oh, yes," Lottie smiled. "I was so glad I had learned about starting a school when I lived in Georgia. That earlier experience has really helped me, ten thousand miles away in China. Whenever I talked to the mothers about a school for their daughters, their eyes lit up.

"So many mothers told me how they wished *they* could have learned to read and write. One young mother said to me, 'Do you think after my daughter learns, she could help me learn to read?' She was excited when I agreed I thought that would be a lovely thing for her daughter to do.

"Of course," Lottie admitted, "not every father was as easily persuaded." She looked a bit indignant when she recalled, "I even had one father say to me, 'Send my daughter to school? Ha! I'd sooner send my cow. It could learn better!'" Lottie gave a little grin when she told the end of that story, "However, I talked him around (persuaded him), and he allowed his little girl to come to school. Was he ever surprised when he heard her actually reading — reading every bit as well as did his son. He beamed with pride!"

Lottie told of one of the most rewarding things about the whole school. "When I talked to those mothers about schooling for their daughters, they needed to understand that we would unbind their girls' little feet so they could grow normally. If you unbound them while they were still young, the feet could grow normally. However, if you waited too many years, it was too late. The bones in the toes would already be broken."

Lottie sighed as she recalled those early days and the dreadful problem of foot-binding. "I recall so many mothers weeping. Each one told me how painful it had been to have her *own* feet bound when she was young. One mother explained that it was the most terrible pain she had ever endured in her whole life." Lottie shook her gray head in disbelief, "Several described to me how their *own* mothers had cried as they had to pull those cloth bindings tighter and tighter every day. Those mothers suffered right along with their little four- and five-year-old girls."

Marion interrupted, a look of pain on her own sweet face, "But, Aunt Lottie, I just wonder *why* those mothers had to bind the girls' feet? It makes no sense."

Lottie gave a deep sigh and shook her head, "I absolutely agree, Marion. It sounds so cruel to us, and it is indeed cruel.

"But, you see, it was an ancient custom that started many hundreds of years ago. Men were always more important than women in China." She narrowed her eyes and cocked her head to one side as she often did when puzzling over something. "I think it was their way of showing that men felt superior. Women with tiny feet would be dependent on them, so the men somehow decided that tiny feet were beautiful. Obviously," she gave a little "humph" of a sound, "they didn't consider the pain they were inflicting."

As she concluded the foot-binding story, Lottie beamed with satisfaction. "I get so much joy from seeing girls grow up with unbound feet. Studying and learning is, in a way, like unbinding their minds. I love seeing their minds take wing. Nothing pleases me more than watching our young students run and play at recess time. Now they can do that without pain."

Lottie smiled, "And, now — *now* —" she repeated, "we have quite a few missionaries here in north China, and we have begun sixteen schools. There are thousands of pupils. Just think, all of these students have learned to read and write and can study God's message in their own language. After so many years, a lot of my former students are now teachers themselves. They are telling *more* little children about God's love. That makes my heart feel so good."

"Do the Chinese girls in your schools do their memory work out loud, Aunt Lottie?" asked a curious Edith. "Doesn't it get loud when everyone is speaking all at the same time?"

Miss Moon acknowledged that the classrooms were noisy. "However," she noted, "that is the way Chinese have learned for centuries. They learn to shut off their ears to the sounds all around them."

Lottie's eyes twinkled, "Let me tell you what the girls did this winter. Can you believe, our class of fourth-year girls all memorized the entire Gospel of Mark! Just think of hearing all those girls recite all of that!"

The three MKs' eyes were wide with surprise. "Oh, my goodness," Rachel confessed, "I can't quote all of that!"

Lottie laughed in reply, "Well, I couldn't either, until I heard it so many times!"

As the girls prepared to go to bed that night, Rachel told Aunt Lottie what was on the minds of each sister. "Aunt Lottie, you know that Daddy is going to come get us tomorrow." Her voice caught a little bit, "We have loved being here with you. You feel like our special friend, our *wiser* friend, of course." There was a smile in Rachel's voice as she added, "And you are the best storyteller of anyone we know!"

Rachel, Edith, and Marion each hugged her Aunt Lottie. In turn, Lottie kissed each young cheek as she assured her MK friends, "Girls, I am already looking forward to you coming back in June. I promise," there was a smile in her voice, "I will have lots more stories to share! I want to 'take you' — in story time, that is — to the villages. Some strange and funny things happened there!"

The Rest of the Story

A great harvest of saved lives came from the many schools begun by Baptist missionaries in China. Thousands of teachers, preachers, doctors, and nurses resulted from the schools built and supported by Baptists through the many years. Lottie Moon became somewhat of a legend to the younger missionaries who were arriving in China during the early twentieth century. Her brilliance was widely recognized, and she used that brilliance in dedicated ministry to God.

Lottie worked in Tengzhou *(Duhng Joe)* with two missionary men who could not get along with each other. However, the gracious Miss Moon was able to remain friends with both of them. She worked with each one in spite of their great differences. Lottie was the "diplomat" of the Tengzhou mission station.

Beyond all the praise that came her way, nothing was more treasured than the love the Chinese people had come to feel for their beloved "Heavenly Book Visitor." The American missionaries were in awe of the degree to which Lottie Moon identified with the people of China. Many times, she would say to a friend, "China is my home. America is like a foreign country to me now." The believers in that vast land felt the very same way. Lottie Moon was one of them. Once a "foreign devil," Lottie Moon ever after was known as their cherished "Heavenly Book Visitor."

Extra Credit

Explore online, or in a library, how schools in China and schools in America are different. Find out how many students are enrolled in schools in China and how many in the United States. Which country has a higher percentage of students who go to college?

The house at the Little Crossroads – Lottie Moon's home (and headquarters) in China.
(Photo courtesy of International Mission Board)

CHAPTER SIX

LOTTIE TAKES HER SLEEPING ROLL

"Father," Marion asked for about the tenth time, "are we nearly there, please?"

Rev. Newton grinned and patiently answered, "Marion, my answer is a bit better this time, for we should be there in about an hour." His eight-year-old bounced with excitement. Of course, they all bounced a good bit in the horse cart transporting them from Hwangshien (*Hwahng She Ann*) to Tengzhou (*Duhng Joe*). Father had a meeting in that city, and the three girls were riding with him. They had been waiting five months for this summer visit with Aunt Lottie.

Daily studies with Mama had consumed their time for most of those months. Father helped in the classroom when he had a chance, but it was mostly Mama who guided their studies. She had attended the famous Vassar College in New York and knew a lot about teaching. Most of the time, Mary Newton was gentle and patient, but the girls knew better than to try her patience too far. After all, they were the oldest of the many Newton siblings and Mama needed their help. Rachel, the oldest, was already her mother's assistant in the classroom. Her youngest sisters, Roby and Helen, were six and seven now. Rachel helped teach them every day.

Riding along the bumpy road, Rachel recalled how bleak it looked last January when they made the same trip. It was June now, and the countryside was lush and green. Fields of newly planted rice paddies were visible for miles around. Of course, the odor of the fertilizer helping the rice grow was pretty overpowering, but the Newton girls were used to it.

Edith had just had her eleventh birthday and was eager to see if she was now taller than Aunt Lottie. They had measured exactly the same height last winter, but Mama kept telling Edith that she was going through a growth spurt. Eight-year-old Marion had grown a lot as well. She, too, was almost Aunt Lottie's height. Rachel, meanwhile, was nearing her thirteenth birthday and was excited about becoming a teenager.

Much excitement was heard all around as their cart pulled into the courtyard at Lottie Moon's home at Little Crossroads. Each girl hugged Aunt Lottie fiercely. She exclaimed about how they had grown, even beyond her expectations. Silently, the sisters observed with some concern that the long winter had taken its toll on their beloved "aunt." Lottie Moon looked older, her hair thinner and with more gray. Her eyes looked tired, but they twinkled with joy upon seeing the Newton sisters.

"Oh, girls," Lottie beamed, "I have needed a lift of heart and spirits.

You are just the medicine the doctor ordered. We will have fun talking and catching up on all that has happened!"

"Aunt Lottie," Rachel had a smile in her voice, "all of us have been excited just thinking about story time each evening after your day's work. You always have some surprising memories to share. You make us feel just like we were right there with you when it happened."

As she led the girls inside, Lottie smiled and said, "Well, girls, a lot has happened since you were here, and I have more stories to tell than time to tell them in! We'll give it a good try, though. And we will start tonight."

Shortly after supper, Marion popped her curly head around the door of the sitting room. She smiled as she saw Miss Moon already in her favorite reading chair, her feet propped up on the little footstool. "Aunt Lottie, is it story time yet? I'll call Rachel and Edith if you're ready."

Lottie smiled as she removed her reading glasses to rub around her tired eyes. "Of course. I'm always ready for stories."

In minutes, the three girls were seated at Lottie's feet for their favorite time of the day. No one could tell a tale quite like their Aunt Lottie. She was in her early seventies, and time, poor health, and hard living conditions had taken their toll on her small body. She looked older than her age, her hair now all gray and wispy, her skin wrinkled by weather, time, and too many cares. It had been a most difficult year. Nonetheless, each girl was convinced Aunt Lottie's heart was as young as ever.

Looking fondly at her three MK friends, Lottie smiled. "Now, where were we in our stories in January? Who can remind me?"

Rachel spoke up, "Remember? Right before we went home in January, you told us about unbinding the feet of the little girls at your school. Well, Mama told us just a few weeks ago that the new revolutionary government announced a new law that prohibits parents from binding their girls' feet. Have you heard that also?"

Lottie smiled, "Indeed I have, and that is a great step in the right direction for all the girls of China." Lottie changed the subject, "And, speaking of the new revolutionary government, I know all of you are aware of the fighting that has been going on all over China."

The Newton sisters nodded. The country was experiencing many changes. For thousands of years, China had been led by emperors and imperial rule. Now, China was suddenly a brand-new republic, and change was everywhere.

Lottie remarked, "I've got some stories about the war to tell you later, but let's get back to our 'once upon a time in the villages' days. It started way back in the 1870s." All three girls looked eager.

Settling comfortably into her chair, Lottie began, "I had scarcely arrived and started language study when Sally Holmes took me for a visit to nearby villages. Sally and her husband were the very first missionaries in Tengzhou *(Duhng Joe)*. They came here over fifty years ago. I wish you girls could have known Sally. She was remarkable. She never ran out of energy!"

Rachel grinned and spoke, "Sort of like you, Aunt Lottie?"

Lottie shook her head back and forth. "Sally could outdo me any day. Listen to her story. When Sally was expecting their baby's birth, Mr. Holmes went into the countryside to preach, but he was set upon and killed by bandits." The girls' eyes grew wide.

Lottie continued, "All the mission advisors and the Foreign Mission Board staff begged Sally to go back to America. She refused," Lottie explained. "When her little son, Landrum, was born, everyone again pleaded with her to leave. They thought it was too dangerous for a woman and her baby to be alone in a foreign country. But Sally was so determined and so strong. She told the mission she would *not* go back to America. She would stay here and work. And work she did!" Miss Moon's face was alight with admiration.

"Sally had spunk! She refused to give up. She was focused on doing what God wanted her to do. Sally trained me in village work. Can you believe that amazing lady in one year's time visited and shared the gospel in over four hundred villages?" The girls' looked impressed.

Lottie continued, "Sometimes when we went to a new town, we were the first foreigners the people there had ever seen. Just picture what that was like." Lottie grinned, "I finally got used to villagers fingering my clothes and touching my hair and feeling my white skin.

"When we arrived in a village, all the people — first the women and children, and then many men — rushed to inspect the strange foreigners. Sally took the women under one tree, and I took the children under another. At first, of course, I needed to have a Chinese Christian from Tengzhou to translate for me. However, I quickly became able to tell the Bible stories in simple Chinese and show Bible pictures that we took along. That was high entertainment for the villagers, most of whom could not read or write. They listened so carefully as we spoke and read to them from the Bible."

"What about singing, Aunt Lottie? Did they like to sing?" asked Marion. "I'd like to have been there with you," she confided.

Lottie smiled and clapped her hands, "I would have liked that too, Marion. They would have loved seeing a 'foreign' child! And, yes, they loved to sing. They kept asking for more songs. Who can guess what their favorite song was?" Lottie cocked her head to one side.

Rachel smiled, "I have an idea it was 'Jesus Loves Me.'"

"You are correct, Rachel," Lottie instantly replied. "The children and Sally and I all loved that song. Contained in that one simple song is the wonderful message of how Jesus loves each of us. You know the words, don't you? Let's sing it in both English and Chinese." The four of them sang together and harmonized their voices.

Lottie explained to the girls, "You remember we talked about how difficult it was at first to get behind the closed doors of homes in the city? Well, it wasn't that way in the villages. Hearts were open there, and receptive to the gospel story. The people of the villages were like a ripe field, just waiting to be harvested."

"Where did you stay in the villages, Aunt Lottie? I don't think those small places have many inns," Rachel asked.

"You are exactly right," Lottie agreed. "So that is why we would take along our sleeping rolls. *Kangs* (*kahngs*) were beds in the homes, or inns, literally made of bricks. All of you have seen these *kangs*, haven't you?"

Three heads nodded up and down, and Rachel spoke, "And are they ever hard! I know in the winter they feel pretty good because there is a pipe bringing heat from the stove. That doesn't make them soft, though!" Rachel gave a little shudder.

"So true," Lottie agreed, "but even *harder* was the challenge of having absolutely no privacy! There were always eyes — at the doors, at the window — staring in at the strange *yahng gway dzuhs*, or foreign devils. After I learned the language better, Mrs. Mung (*Muhng*), a dear Christian lady from our city church, traveled with me. We visited three or four villages a day. Then the following morning, we headed out to three or four more.

"Back in those days, women couldn't teach or preach to men, of course. However, we missionaries couldn't help it if the village men came to the fringes of the crowd of women and children and listened. I loved village work," Lottie's weary face was alive with joy. "Such eagerness, such drinking in of the truth, I had never before seen. Many women and children — and, yes, even men — believed. That made my heart so happy."

Edith asked, "Aunt Lottie, didn't those trips make you really tired after a while?"

Lottie sighed and explained, "Oh, yes. Some nights I was so tired, I thought I could not utter another word. My lips felt dry and parched," and she touched her lips. "My throat was raw from teaching so long. Worst of all, my stomach rebelled against food that I hesitate to even describe. But, about then," she added with a bright gleam in her eye, "someone would come up and say, '*Moo Lah Dee Law Shur* (Teacher Miss Moon), just how *does* God enter my heart? How can I find peace?' Well, I ask you girls, how could I *not* speak when I know the words of life?

"One of my biggest jobs as a missionary has been to write back to America, to our mission board, and to Baptist churches and pastors. I also write to women's missionary societies and tell them what God is doing in China. There is so much work to be done, and so few of us to do it. I asked the mission board, 'What can Baptists be thinking of to send one man and three women for thirty million souls in north China?'

"Furthermore, you can't imagine how it felt to have so many questions asked of you in every village. The first question was nearly always, 'How old are you?' followed by, 'Where are you from?' and 'Are you married?' When I said 'no,' the women exclaimed in amazement, 'What! You have no mother-in-law?' Sometimes, when people kept staring on and on, I would ask them, '*Why* are you staring?' and one would answer, 'Forgive us, Miss Moon. You see, we have never seen a Heavenly Person before.'"

Marion sounded awed, "It must have been so hard, Aunt Lottie. How did you ever manage to keep up such tiring work?"

Lottie gave a little shake of her head, "Child, I wondered that same thing many a night. But, do you know, the next morning I always got up and started afresh. The dirt and stares, the indigestible food and tiredness, were all worth it when a new soul trusted in Christ. Women believed, children believed, and, yes, many men as well. That was the greatest heart-lifter of all."

Lottie drew in a deep breath, "All the weeks in the villages were hard on my body, but it was a joy at the very same time. Sometimes I would come back here to my house at Little Crossroads to regain energy. While here, I would work with the teachers I had in place at the school, rest up, then head back to the villages again. I always took along material to read at night by lantern light."

Lottie settled again into her chair and recalled an article she had read in one of the state Baptist papers from America. "Girls," she related, "one night I was especially tired. My throat was sore, and my stomach felt absolutely miserable. I read in one of our state papers that they were announcing the 'end of the days of missionary hardships.' Ha! I immediately wrote back to the paper and asked them if they felt it might be a hardship for *them* to sleep on a brick bed. What about eating all strange food and living for weeks at a time in houses with dirt floors and no toilets?" Lottie gave a little grin, "After that letter, I never found any more articles about the *easy* life of a missionary!"

"Aunt Lottie," Rachel shook her head back and forth in sympathy, "was that about the time furloughs started, so missionaries could get some rest?"

Miss Moon nodded and replied, "Let me tell you about furloughs. But," she stopped again, "we'll have to do that later." Checking her lapel watch, she continued, "There is more time for stories tomorrow. But it's off to bed now. I'm so happy you girls are back. You help me feel young until I happen to look in a mirror!"

The Rest of the Story

Recounting the village adventures of Lottie Moon over her thirty-nine years of missions service would fill more than one book. Village work was her favorite ministry, but also the one that took the greatest toll on her body. To Lottie, it was worth all the effort, for it was her great happiness to see numbers of souls born into God's kingdom. On one particular village journey, she and Sally Holmes teamed up with Chinese friend and pastor, Mr. Dzoong. They traveled to his home village to preach the gospel. He was a believer with a peaceful smile and a glowing face. Lottie said of him, "To be with Mr. Dzoong is to know he has been with Jesus."

On their way to the village, they gathered a crowd of some thirty women and children. As usual, the women wanted to know if she was "*nánde*" (*nahn duh*, a man) or "*nyúde*" (*new duh*, a woman). Lottie good-naturedly assured them she was a woman. The men of the village pleaded to be allowed to listen to the good news as well. Lottie wrote to the mission board, "I hope you won't think me desperately unfeminine (for speaking to men), but I spoke to them all. I should not have dared to remain silent with so many souls before me sunk in darkness."

Extra Credit

It's easy to learn the Chinese words to the chorus of Lottie Moon's favorite hymn, "Jesus Loves Me." Learn it in this easy-to-follow romanization:

Jew Yeh Sue Eye Woe
Jew Yeh Sue Eye Woe
Jew Yeh Sue Eye Woe
Yo Shun Shoo Gaw Sue Woe

Lottie's favorite footstool, now at National Woman's Missionary Union, Birmingham, Alabama

Sketch of Lottie Moon in 1901 (By Lori Windsor Hunt)

CHAPTER SEVEN

LOTTIE THE LETTER WRITER

Aunt Lottie was looking really tired this evening, and the Newton girls didn't want to waste her time. They quickly assembled in the sitting room. Rachel in particular was concerned about her elderly friend's failing health. Aunt Lottie was walking more slowly now, and her steps were often unsteady. Rachel's keen eyes noted that she also seemed smaller than ever. The sisters helped her in little ways to make her more comfortable.

Lottie sighed and sank into her favorite chair, propping her feet on her little footstool. Stifling a yawn, she apologized, "I'm sorry, dear girls, for yawning, but the day has been long."

"Oh, Aunt Lottie," Rachel hastily said, "we don't want to tire you even more."

Lottie smiled in her gentle way that always touched their hearts, "I'm never too tired for you girls. Let me jump right in and tell you about how furloughs finally started. Rachel, you are our walking dictionary. What is a furlough?"

Rachel grinned and suggested, "I think it means a time for rest and relaxation."

Lottie's eyes twinkled. "Absolutely correct! It so happened that I had not been here very long before I could see that some of our missionaries were absolutely exhausted. They had been working for years with no relief. They had very little medical care, and some were so burdened about the needs all around that they felt helpless. I wanted to help. So, I wrote letters. Letter writing is something I do a lot of, you know," and three young heads nodded vigorously. They had heard that Aunt Lottie was north China's best letter writer. For years, she had been the one to write reports and requests to the Foreign Mission Board. She was highly influential with the board and knew just how to word a letter.

Lottie began her story, "I soon began writing to Dr. Tupper about missionaries needing help. They needed occasional furloughs to rest their bodies and their spirits and minds. I told him over and over how the other mission boards had already realized this. Methodists and the Presbyterians worked for five or seven years in China and then had a furlough. As I observed to Dr. Tupper, 'We Southern Baptists expect our missionaries to stay for life. It is as if you were saying to a soldier you were sending to the front lines, 'Do battle with the enemy. Mind, no furloughs! We expect you to fall on the field.'" Lottie shook her head in dismay as she reflected on the many Baptists who just didn't understand the need for furloughs.

Rachel's eyes grew large, "You were brave to write so boldly, Aunt Lottie!"

"Not really," Lottie retorted. "I was just worried about our missionaries staying alive!"

Lottie continued. "I got out my pen again and again and wrote to Dr. Tupper about what was happening. I also learned that Dr. Roswell Graves, our wonderful pioneer missionary doctor in south China, was telling our board the very same thing." Lottie heaved a sigh and then added, "I explained to Dr. Tupper, 'I have seen missionaries all around me, failing physically, suffering nervous breakdowns, even dying. We are falling on the field. Help!'"

The girls sat big-eyed as Lottie nodded her head and ended, "Well, finally the board got the idea, and started allowing furloughs. But," she shook her head in resignation, "our Baptist board *still* has no regular system. Nonetheless, as opposed to having *no* relief and rest, it is better than *no* furloughs at all!"

Rachel, always eager to know more about any story, inquired, "Aunt Lottie, you had been here long years before furloughs ever started. When furloughs were first approved, did you take one right away so you could get some rest too?"

Lottie shook her head. "Ah, no. You see, I had to say to the board, 'How can I leave now, when there is nobody to stand in the gap, to do the work while I am gone?'" She got that distant look in her eyes, as if reliving those days in the last century.

Lottie confessed, "I waited fourteen years before that first furlough. *Finally,* a reinforcement arrived." The girls knew when Lottie got that faraway look, she was remembering scenes from long ago. Lottie's eyes grew damp with tears, "I was still afraid of falling on the field just like

I had seen happen to others. But, thank God, He kept me going until a reinforcement arrived."

She waited a few moments before explaining to her young friends, "To be truthful, I need to tell you one of the biggest problems I've ever faced. But first, you tell me what *you* feel would be a really big problem. Marion, what do you think?" and she smiled directly at her youngest MK guest.

"Well-l-l," Marion dragged the word out while she thought, "maybe eating really strange and smelly food that is nasty to swallow!"

Lottie grinned and nodded, "Good guess, Marion. Some of the food is pretty awful to get down. But that's not the worst."

Edith took a turn, "Aunt Lottie, is it all those crawly bugs that get in your sleeping roll? Or the rats you see scuttling around in the corners, or you hear scurrying around in the dark at night?" and she gave a little shiver.

Rachel cocked her head to one side and added her contribution, "Maybe it is the people in the villages who keep staring, and watching everything you do, and touching your clothes and your white skin and asking you every minute what you are doing."

Lottie smiled and nodded at each idea, "Good guesses, girls. I must admit, every one of those is very annoying and sometimes downright disgusting! Edith, I recall two nights when I had rats scuttle right over my blanket!" Edith giggled and shivered all at the same time.

"But even worse than all that," Lottie explained, "was one truly dreadful thing: loneliness. That was my constant enemy. You remember how I grew up in a big family? There was always lots of noise and activity and companionship. But, out in all those villages, I sometimes went for weeks on end without speaking English. I had no one with whom I could just chat and visit, like I do with you dear girls — someone I could relax with. I missed that so much." Lottie bit her lower lip and sighed deeply as she recalled the empty feeling of loneliness.

"In one of the letters to Dr. Tupper, I just came out and admitted, 'I am bored to death with living alone. I don't find my own society either agreeable or edifying.' Dr. Tupper was a good friend, and he tried to encourage me. One time he even wrote, 'I estimate a single woman in China is worth two married men.'" Lottie laughed when she concluded, "I passed that compliment on to our other single ladies when I saw them. It made them smile too!"

Lottie then told how she continually wrote to Baptists in America about the need for a special offering so that *more* missionaries could be sent. "I suggested they start a missions offering at Christmas time, writing, 'Need it be said why the weeks before Christmas are chosen? Is not the festive season, when family and friends exchange gifts in memory of the gift of God, the most appropriate time to consecrate a portion of our abounding riches and scant poverty, to send forth the good news into all the world?'"

She concluded by saying, "I ended that letter with these words: 'I wonder how many of us *really* believe that it is more blessed to give than to receive? How many are there among us who believe that because "Jesus Paid It All," they need pay *nothing*?' And, do you know, Baptists started just such an offering. And that is why more missionaries have been able to come!"

Lottie shifted in her easy chair and explained, "I'm skipping ahead now to furlough, but tomorrow I'll return to another adventure story of mine here in China. Right now, let's go together to 1891. At long last — a furlough. I boarded the ship, the *Empress of China,* in Shanghai. For all that long voyage, I was terribly seasick and suffered agonizing headaches. Finally," and she smiled a weary smile at the memory, "after fourteen years I was at long last back in America. I could get some rest to restore my body and my heart and spirit too. To be honest, I felt nearly drained dry!"

"Oh, Aunt Lottie," Edith's beautiful brown eyes teared up in sympathy, "I am so glad you didn't 'fall on the field.' "

Lottie gently touched Edith's cheek as she smiled, "That was a lifesaver for me, Edith. And I did a lot of resting the first months back in America. I lived with my sister Edmonia in a cozy little four-room house. Every day I would walk for miles and enjoy the quiet and the beauty around me. God refreshed my soul — which is just what it needed. That way I could return to China, strong and renewed.

"Of course, I soon began speaking in churches and to mission groups, telling them what God was doing in China. I was so happy, because all the letter writing had paid off and Baptist women had finally organized. They formed a union to support missions! I'm sure that your mother, Mary, has told you how the various state missionary groups came together and became Woman's Missionary Union. Miss Annie Armstrong was the new leader. They were having their annual meeting that May in Birmingham, Alabama. I was thrilled to attend and meet Miss Annie!" Lottie chuckled, "Rachel, if I remember correctly, that was the year you came to China as a little toddler!" Rachel smiled and nodded, pleased that Aunt Lottie remembered.

Lottie's eyes sparkled as she told the girls, "I saw several old friends there. One of my dearest college friends was now the WMU president from Mississippi. We had a grand reunion. Julia Toy and I had graduated together over thirty years earlier."

Lottie beamed when recalling that national woman's missionary meeting. "I was delighted to meet the new president," Lottie smiled broadly, "a young woman from North Carolina named Fannie Heck. She was regal and beautiful and about half my age! Fannie was a gifted leader and seemed honored to meet this seasoned old warrior from China. I loved being able to tell all those women about China and our schools and the joy of work in the villages. And you may be sure I told them how much we need *more* helpers to come."

Lottie gave a little laugh, "I wish you could have seen the stage where we stood that day. There on the platform was Miss Annie Armstrong, tall and queenly at six feet tall. And right next to her stood this wizened little woman from China, who is maybe four-feet-seven-inches tall on a good day!"

The girls grinned, and Rachel exclaimed, "But, Aunt Lottie, you are big in heart!"

"Heart!" Lottie echoed. "Speaking of hearts, I can tell you honestly, Rachel, that I had not long been in America when there came to my heart, as clear as the tones of a crystal bell — China — and I returned with joy.

"One day while I was still in America, a friend asked me, 'Lottie, do you *really* need to go back? You have already given all those years of your life to China. Why don't you stay home?' Do you know what my reply was?" Lottie gave a beautiful smile and answered her own question, "I told her, 'I *am* going home! You see, China has crept into my heart, and set up permanent housekeeping there.'" Lottie shook her head at the thought, "Bugs, strange food, no privacy — I am not wild about those! But this is my home now. I would not trade it for anything."

"Aunt Lottie," Rachel asked, "didn't you start the work in the interior? Mama told us that your bravery always encourages her when she doesn't feel so brave herself!"

Lottie responded, "Actually, Rachel, I did find another home in addition to Tengzhou (*Duhng Joe*). There was not another foreigner living in the whole untouched area called Pingtu (*Ping Do*). But there were masses of people, and no one there knew about the one true God."

About then, Lottie glanced at her little lapel watch and said the inevitable, "Tomorrow! Tomorrow we will go far into the interior!"

Three girls grinned and knew it was time for bed, and for another true story to look forward to.

The Rest of the Story

Lottie's dear friend from college days was her old pal from Mississippi, Julia Toy Johnson. Julia's husband was a pastor in Mississippi, and Julia was the state WMU president. Julia and her husband had wanted to go to Japan as missionaries, but ill health prevented them.

A few of Lottie's close friends believed that she, at one time, was close to getting married. This probable beau was none other than one of her college professors, a brilliant teacher who had planned to go as a missionary himself. Furthermore, he was the brother of Julia Toy, Lottie's college friend. On one occasion, Lottie had actually told a relative that there was going to be a wedding, but it never happened. The last time Lottie was in America, a niece asked her if she had ever been in love. Lottie replied, "Yes, but God had first claim on my life and since the two conflicted, there could be no question about the result."

Extra Credit

Keep learning about Baptist missions history by exploring the life of Dr. Roswell Graves, pioneer missionary doctor in south China. Search for his name on the internet or in library books to learn about this amazing man who impacted many lives. Dr. Graves' mother was Ann Baker Graves, known as the "Mother of WMU." Her story is another fascinating tale that you can research.

CHAPTER EIGHT

LOTTIE ENTERS THE INTERIOR

Lottie smiled at her young guests as they settled at her feet in the sitting room. The girls couldn't picture their Aunt Lottie without her faithful little footstool. It had been made especially for her, and she was much attached to it.

As was her custom, Lottie began, "Once upon a time (that's how she liked her stories to begin), I had a truly exciting new adventure. Let's see, it was 1885, and that's over twenty-five years ago. I was quite young then, and my body was stronger and livelier. Never before had a Southern Baptist woman started a new outpost in missions. My fellow missionaries, however, felt like I should be the one to open such a new venture.

"I frequently thought about those interior towns and villages south and west of us, villages where no one had ever heard about God." Smiling, Lottie continued, "I felt like an explorer, a bit like David Livingstone. I loved reading about his pioneer work in Africa. Of course, moving so far from the big cities meant I would be cut off from comforts and friends, from anyone I knew. I would be a small and insignificant little woman surrounded by the ancient culture of China.

"However," Lottie was thinking aloud, "I knew I wasn't really going to be alone and on my own. Surely God was with me. His Holy Spirit was my guide. I must tell you, never had I felt so dependent on God's Spirit to guide me."

Aunt Lottie described the interior to her attentive listeners, "Pingtu (*Ping Do*) was a walled city and quite well to do. Flourishing fields grew all around it. And," she smiled confidingly, "the people in the city weren't snobby like those in Tengzhou (*Duhng Joe*). And picture this, Pingtu is the twelfth largest population center in the whole world! But not one other foreigner lived there."

Lottie related how she went back to Tengzhou after a month to make plans to move to Pingtu and start work. "You see, my dears, I had learned by that time that work in the villages and countryside succeeds much better than in the cities. This was simply a new challenge. I do love challenges! I found a house to rent — one with four rooms: kitchen, storeroom, passageway, and then my all-purpose room. That's where I lived, slept, and received visitors. My *kang* (bed) was made of mud bricks." Lottie laughed as she saw the girls grinning, "Yes, it was indeed hard, but that's where I slept. I put local straw matting and rugs on the mud floor."

Lottie pictured the setting for her rapt audience. "My mattress went on the *kang*, and I rolled up my sleeping roll as a cushion for the back. I sat cross-legged on it all day and received visitors. I had a new strategy to try out there in Pingtu. I would *first* become friends with my neighbors, and then I could teach them and help them. It took a while, but it worked!

"Now, think with me a moment," Lottie said, "I used one particular strategy for meeting people that I had used in Tengzhou. What would you guess that to be?" Lottie smiled at the three girls.

Marion was first to respond, "Oh, Aunt Lottie, I'll guess it was cookies! Just like those we had tonight!"

"And you would be correct, Marion. Little Pingtu children love cookies just like children in Tengzhou." Lottie gave a little chuckle. "Right at first, the children and their parents waved away the cookies I offered. They were alarmed, and feared the cookies might be poison offered to them by this *yahng gway dzuhs* (foreign devil). Of course, those fresh, warm cookies proved to be too tempting — and, suddenly, everyone wanted one and then another one. Next, their parents would come with some little goody for me. Before you knew it, I was invited into their homes and became their friend."

Lottie described her new plan to make children and their mothers feel comfortable around her. She began dressing in traditional Chinese clothes. With her dark hair, suntanned face, and her hair slicked back in a bun, she looked quite like one of them. Women became more friendly, and people no longer asked, "*Ni nánde (nan duh)? Ni nyúde (new duh)*?": "Are you a man or a woman?"

Lottie related that a Christian couple from her church in Tengzhou came back to their original home in Pingtu. They helped Lottie with many things, including cooking for her. At least she liked rice, and she had brought her American-style flour so she could make those tempting cookies. "Girls," Lottie confessed, "after I had been there several months, I realized that the *hardest* thing was not being able to hear English spoken. Sometimes," and Lottie got a little emotional even telling it, "I longed to hear the language of my youth.

"While I was in the interior, something dawned on me," Lottie told the sisters. "God's Word became newly precious and was my companion. As I read the Bible, it seemed like I was conversing with my dear friend and Heavenly Father.

"I knew it was important not to get completely burned out. I had seen that happen to far too many missionary friends. So, I returned here to Tengzhou *(Duhng Joe)* in the summer when it got really hot. It is a bit cooler here than Pingtu."

Then Lottie's eyes filled with unshed tears. "Girls, it was so lonely. I pray that no missionary will have to be as lonely I have been. And yet," she drew in a deep breath, "somehow, I felt the power, and the comfort, and the very *presence* of the Holy Spirit as never before in my life." The eyes of the three young MKs seated there on the floor welled up with tears of sympathy.

Lottie gave a little sniff and paused a moment to use her handker-chief. Smiling tremulously, she continued, "But, every moment of loneliness was *more* than worth it, when someone like young Miss Wang came up to me, right after her baptism and whispered in my ear, 'Oh, Miss Moon, how can I ever thank you aright for having come to bring to *me* the good news of salvation?'"

Lottie shifted in her chair as if shifting scenes in her story, "After a few months of rest and checking on my schools, I headed back to Pingtu. This time, the people welcomed me like one of them. I would sit many hours a day on my *kang*, teaching visitors about God's love and how they could know him too. Also, knowing how important exercise was, I took time every day to walk and visit. People constantly stopped me with questions, many wanting to know about God. I loved it!"

Rachel asked, "Aunt Lottie, were you ever invited into their homes?"

"Oh yes," Lottie beamed. "I ended up with many women inviting me in and wanting to learn more about eternal life and how to obtain it. They were hungry to hear about a God who loved them." She declared, "It had never been like this in Tengzhou. I loved the way people were hungry to know about a Savior.

"Men would inquire as well. Of course, I told them, just as I told the women and children, about the way to eternal life. In several homes," Lottie smiled at the memory, "women would thrust their daughters in front of me, saying, 'Teach them too, please. They can learn more quickly than we!'"

Lottie reminded the sisters, "Each time I wrote our board and Baptists in America, I pleaded with them to send more women for this wonderful frontier work. It became a sacred adventure."

Again, Lottie shifted in her chair, "Just then, would you believe, the board rather reluctantly granted furloughs. I knew I was overdue for one. But," she drew in a long breath before shaking her head and saying, "how could I leave when there was *no one* to come to Pingtu and do the work while I was away? In my mind, I pictured being in Virginia again. I longed to be with my dear sister Edmonia and get some rest. Then I thought of those dear souls around me, took a deep breath, and told the board I couldn't leave quite yet."

Rachel spoke with sympathy in her every word, "Oh, Aunt Lottie, you were so tired, though. How could you stand it?"

Lottie smiled gently, "Only by God's grace, dear girl. And I had the reward of seeing so many people come to know the Lord. About that same time, three elderly men came from Shaling (*Shah Ling*), a prosperous little village about ten miles away. The leading village elder was Dan Ho-bang (*Dahn Ho Bahng*). He had heard about a man called Jesus who could remove sins from people. And he had heard of a Heavenly Book Visitor in Pingtu. Could she come to their humble village and tell them the news about this Jesus?"

Lottie's face was alight at the memory of that visit. She answered her own question, "Could she go? Oh, yes, she could! I went to Shaling to teach the 'Jesus way.' In just three weeks' time, old Mr. Dan and five others trusted God's grace. It was so exciting! I wrote Martha Crawford to come help, and she came for several weeks. What joy! We told the story of redemption. We taught them hymns." Lottie paused, "And which was their favorite?"

All three girls chimed up, "Jesus Loves Me!"

Lottie smiled and nodded. "And they memorized many Scripture passages. So many couldn't read, but by memorizing, they could keep God's Word in their hearts."

Lottie added, "Martha and I stayed in Mr. Dan's home. We used the village threshing floor for our meeting place, and we taught great crowds. I had never before seen hearts so ready to hear! It was incredible to me, really, how the *men* would come to hear. They would sit in an adjoining room. For the first time in my years here in China, it was the men who were the first to respond. Clearly, there were no men of our mission there in Shaling to teach them. But I knew their souls were also important. So, no matter the custom, I taught them the Word of God and prepared them to be leaders.

"Girls," Lottie's face was glowing now, "twenty of the fifty village families believed. We established the first church in the interior of China. Those dear people were the joy of my heart!" The Newton sisters clapped their hands at learning about the wonderful response in Shaling as well as in Pingtu. Lottie added, "Several of our men missionaries came, and we baptized numbers of believers. And, from that first church, more churches were organized because of those faithful believers.

"That year, I had planned to rest in Tengzhou *(Duhng Joe)*, as had become my custom, during the hottest months," said Lottie. "However, the missionaries in Chinkiang *(Juhn Jyahng)* in central China asked me to come to their city and teach the missionary wives how to witness to the women there. Before I left, the entire group asked me to move to Chinkiang to work with them." Lottie smiled and shook her head, saying, "How could I do that? I was needed in Pingtu and Shaling!"

Lottie continued, "When I returned to my house at Little Crossroads, it took a few weeks to reorganize and prepare to go back to Shaling. But early one morning, there was a knock on my gate. Two of the new believers from Shaling had *walked* the entire 120 miles from Shaling! They said the people of Shaling had grown anxious about me. They wanted to know if I could come back." Lottie's eyes misted up again at the memory. "Such hunger for God and His Word. I packed quickly and returned to Shaling. What a reunion I had with those precious villagers!"

Lottie declared that never in her many years in China had she seen response like that in Shaling. One young man came and asked her to explain to him how he could obtain that eternal life. Lottie smiled, "He told me, 'I can't help believing. I can't help acting out my beliefs!'

"It was not like that all the time, of course," Lottie continued. "There was persecution for some believers because they were no longer worshipping their ancestors. Old Mr. Dan *(Dahn)* himself was persecuted and beaten, but he stood firm. How his faith did shine."

Then, the eagerly attentive girls noticed Aunt Lottie glancing at her watch. They knew what that meant. Sure enough, Lottie exclaimed, "Oh, dear. Look at the time! I got so excited about Shaling village that I forgot how late it has grown."

As the girls reluctantly got to their feet, Lottie added, "Be prepared for tomorrow. There will be a special story about a believer. But there will also be war and travel and famine, and *more* war! I realize you girls can't stay much longer on this visit, but I am eager to share my heart with you before you go home."

"Oh, Aunt Lottie," Rachel spoke up as they headed to bed, "we treasure your life stories. I wish you had them all written down."

Edith joined in, "They are already written on our hearts!"

The Rest of the Story

Lottie Moon did not tell the story of her personal involvement with protecting the Shaling and Pingtu believers from persecution. However, those accounts were shared by her fellow missionaries who learned of them through the Chinese believers. This persecution began around 1890, when God's work had started thriving in that frontier area. Mr. Dan *(Dahn)*, the patriarch of Shaling village, was persecuted by his own relatives when he refused to worship the ancestral tablets in his home. They bound his hands and feet and strung him on a pole. Then, they viciously beat him.

The persecution spread to other believers, and their lives were in danger. Lottie Moon heard of the torturing and the threats to destroy the Shaling church. She placed her own frail little body between the believers and those who were persecuting them. She told the mob, "If you attempt to destroy this church, you will have to kill me first. Jesus gave Himself for us Christians. Now I am ready to die for Him."

One of the mob stepped forward to kill her, but the others stopped him. Lottie told the terrified Christians, "Only believe, don't fear. Our Master, Jesus, always watches over us. No matter what, Jesus will surely overcome it." And, miraculously, the mob turned and left.

Extra Credit

Research the gripping story of missions work in the interior of

China during the late nineteenth and early twentieth centuries. An excellent source of information is Catherine Allen's *The New Lottie Moon Story*. The fascinating details of pioneer outreach in north China are a remarkable account of God at work.

Lottie Moon's Pingtu house when she lived there.

Author with Mr. Swun, owner of the house, who was born there in 1916.

CHAPTER NINE

LOTTIE FACES FAMINE AND FIGHTING

Rachel Newton was worried. During this visit, she was paying close attention to Aunt Lottie's health. Her dearest "aunt" seemed to be failing rapidly. *Not her mind,* Rachel thought, *it is her walking, and how she holds on to furniture getting from one spot to another.* Rachel also realized Aunt Lottie was not eating much. She was tiny. Of course, lack of strength made her energy flag, and she got tired much too easily. Rachel also noticed that Lottie's eyes were growing weaker; she didn't even notice the little bugs in the cereal. Clearly, Li Tai Tai (*Lee Tie Tie*), her elderly cook, could not see them either. Rachel determined to tell her parents about the situation. Maybe they could do something to help.

Outwardly, Lottie seemed much the same. As they gathered for story time, she was as cheerful as ever. "My dear young friends," Lottie nodded to each of the three, "I regret that this will be our last story time this spring. I realize you must return home tomorrow. But just think, our north China mission meeting is coming up soon and I will see you there."

All three girls agreed about how hard it was to leave. Edith smiled, "But Aunt Lottie, at least we can see you again soon!"

"My dear MKs, we are starting adventures tonight with danger and fighting," Lottie began, "and then terrible famine and even *more* fighting!" She shook her head in dismay, "I don't often speak about these sad things, because every time I do, it makes me feel sad all over again! Rachel," Lottie spoke directly to the twelve-year-old, "I believe the Boxer Rebellion began about the time you were born!"

Lottie summed up the situation in China in late 1899, explaining, "Wicked Empress Dowager Tsu Chi (*Tsuu Chee*) was like a dictator. She was both anti-foreigner and anti-Christian. Tsu Chi encouraged a group of rabble-rousers in the countryside called Boxers. They hated foreigners, especially Christians. They persecuted us at every opportunity. When some of these troublemakers began attacking Christians in Pingtu (*Ping Do*), the US Consul (American official in Chefoo) warned all the missionaries to be very careful. America could not protect them except in the port cities."

The girls paid close attention as Lottie told of danger lying all around. She said, "I kept up with government news. Then I heard locally that some of our dear Pingtu Christians were being tortured and thrown into prison on false charges. I knew I must go help them, danger or not." Lottie's face grew very serious as she remembered those terrible days. "First, I got an enclosed sedan chair, just like the local mandarins (officials) use. I put on a man's long Chinese robe and wore an official's cap with a bright red button on it. I slicked my hair back and sat in the chair with my arms folded in front like a mandarin, looking haughtily from right to left. That's what all the mandarins did!" The girls laughed out loud at the mental picture of tiny Lottie Moon looking like a miniature mandarin and getting by with it!

Lottie grinned as well and concluded, "About the time I got to Pingtu, our dear Christian friends were released from prison. I was able to encourage and comfort all our believers, and God protected them. But then," and her face grew solemn, "my presence as a foreigner made it even *more* dangerous for them, so I returned to Tengzhou (*Duhng Joe*). The US Consul ordered all missionaries to leave and helped us get on boats to take us to safety. Some of us went to cities that were far away from the danger. I figured it was going to be some time before we could get back home, so I decided to go to Japan and teach there."

Lottie gave a nostalgic sigh. "Oh, girls, it was a wonderful ten months in that clean, friendly country. I couldn't speak Japanese, but so many wanted to learn English. I could help each day by teaching. Many fine young men were eager to study. Of course, I used the Bible as our textbook. Three of those intelligent young students trusted Christ's grace and began sharing the good news themselves!"

Lottie related how the Boxer Rebellion was finally brought under control, but not before scores of foreigners — mostly missionaries — had died. Several hundred missionaries and thousands of Chinese Christians were persecuted and killed. "My only consolation for the dear Christian friends that I lost," Lottie told her young listeners, "was knowing that they were rejoicing in heaven. I know we will be reunited there."

Lottie stretched and shifted, easing the stiffness in her weary bones. "Girls, forgive my scratchy voice. This old throat started giving me trouble about fifteen years ago, so I try to pamper it. It's the only throat I'll ever have!" Smiling, she continued, "After the Boxer Rebellion, things became peaceful, and the work in the villages and in Pingtu was thriving.

I was overdue for furlough again but could scarcely bring myself to leave when so many were trusting Jesus. However," she nodded, "we had more replacements coming, and that helped me realize there would be missionaries to continue the work. This old body needed some rest. China is *home*, but I knew my family in America was much smaller now. So many were gone. I needed to be with my remaining relatives one more time.

"This time in America, I felt like a visitor. China is my real home. Nonetheless, I had dear ones to see and encourage. Also, Baptists needed to hear how to pray for their missionaries and send more!" Lottie gave a smile that took ten years off her age. "And I was able to tell Baptists about Li Shou Ting (*Lee Show Ting*). His elderly uncle had heard the gospel from me there in Shaling. I gave him a Bible, but he couldn't read, so he took the Bible to his nephew, who was a bright young Confucian scholar. Young Mr. Li came and asked that I teach him." Again, her face glowed with joy. "He not only believed, but he became an evangelist and baptized more than 10,000 believers. In fact," she exclaimed, "just last year he baptized 500 in Pingtu alone!"

Happy tears trickled down her weathered cheeks at the memory. Then her mind returned to leaving America that last time. "I knew this was my last furlough," she told the Newton sisters. "I came home to China, and God has allowed me to keep working for him. More and more people are hearing and believing. That makes my heart happy every day."

Lottie's smile was wide. "I have been able to welcome many new missionaries, just as I welcomed your dear parents ten years ago. More single women and young couples have come, and that encourages my heart. New hands for the harvest of souls! I have been able to help our new workers learn how to study Chinese and adjust to all the new things they face every day. We have even had a few weddings, girls — and those have been beautiful!

"You will enjoy this," Lottie beamed. "When Dr. W.W. Adams came, he stayed here his first year and boarded with me while he studied. I suggested he do a lot of memorizing in Chinese. Guess what his first assignment was?"

The girls looked puzzled, and Lottie explained. "I had him memorize all the verses of 'Jesus Loves Me.'" The girls clapped their hands in glee.

"Edith," Lottie addressed the middle sister, "does your mama work with the missionary society in your Hwangshien (*Hwahng She Ann*) church?"

"Oh yes, Aunt Lottie," Edith responded. "Sometimes we can go with her."

Lottie's eyes twinkled as she nodded, "We also started a missionary society here in my Monument Street church back in 1896. Those women are special." Lottie recalled, "And just last year, we organized the north China Woman's Missionary Union right here in this sitting room."

"Nonetheless," Lottie's face grew serious, "these past two years have been the most difficult of all. You girls, and your family, too, have been living through these same hard days. China has been in great trouble."

All three girls nodded solemnly. Miss Moon got that faraway look again, as if she was seeing the scenes before her eyes. "We had two earth-shaking events hit this country at about the same time." Lottie shook her head in sorrow. "First, famine devastated us here in central and north China, and right along with it, the Revolution."

Rachel, a concerned look in her eyes, asked, "Aunt Lottie, are these elderly little ladies I see in the rooms you have here at Little Crossroads victims of the famine?"

"They are," Lottie responded. "They were literally starving, and how could I eat when they couldn't?" Her face looked drawn with sorrow. "My dear young friends, I know you have seen the suffering all around. In Pingtu (*Ping Do*) I had Christian friends who were eating ground leaves and potato vines." Her eyes clouded over with tears at the memory. "Floods ruined the crops, and there simply was not enough food. People even died along the roadside from starvation."

Lottie was weeping by this time, and the girls attempted to comfort her by patting her arm and murmuring tender words.

Rachel spoke, "Aunt Lottie, since we have been here, we have seen you when children come to your door. You have given each of them food and spoken kind words of encouragement."

Lottie blew her nose and tried to regain her composure. "Of course. How can I eat, and not share with them?" she asked.

Rachel continued, "Aunt Lottie, we have been afraid because of the war too. What do you think brought on the Revolution?"

Lottie thought before replying, "Girls, I think the Boxer Rebellion, just a few years earlier, weakened the old Empress Dowager and the whole Ching Dynasty. Some of the highly educated young adults were tired of the years of oppression. They wanted change, and last year the Revolution began."

All three girls nodded, and Edith said, "We were scared for a while after we left here last winter, Aunt Lottie. Not long after we got home, a message came from the US Consul in Chefoo. It said all Americans had to leave Hwangshien (*Hwahng She Ann*) because the fighting was very close to us." Edith shivered a little bit at the memory.

Marion declared, "I was scared until we got to Chefoo!"

Lottie smiled and nodded, "And rightly so. Your parents had a large family to protect, and you needed to go to safety."

Edith added, "Yes, all our mission families left. Counting all of us children, there were a lot of people leaving. How did you manage, Aunt Lottie?"

Lottie replied, "When I learned that you children and all the missionaries had left, I began thinking about the hospital in Hwangshien (*Hwahng She Ann*). How would they manage with all the missionary doctors and nurses gone?"

Lottie then launched into the story of that frightening time. "I felt compelled to go to the aid of the staff left at the hospital. Fighting was intense along the twenty-mile road, with soldiers of the Ching Dynasty and the revolutionaries engaged in fierce fighting."

Lottie straightened up in her chair and spoke firmly, "I was accompanied by one thing: my faith in God's protection. Miraculously, word spread among the troops on both sides that the Heavenly Book Visitor was traveling to Hwangshien. I passed through enemy lines untouched."

The girls were wide-eyed as Lottie continued, "Upon arrival, I found terrified nurses and staff trying the best they could to cope with the sick and suffering people. Girls, I know a little bit about nursing just from experience, so I helped as much as I could." She smiled and nodded her head up and down, admitting, "I think the main thing I did was put courage in their hearts and a cup of hot tea in their hands."

Lottie finished her account, "Ten days later, our missionary doctors put their own lives at risk to return and help the patients. To their amazement, they arrived to find things in peaceful order. They also found me in charge. Confident that all was now in their good hands, I prepared to return to Tengzhou (*Duhng Joe*). The doctors insisted that a missionary accompany me, so young Cary Daniels volunteered."

Smiling at the memory, Lottie concluded, "News went through the troops on both sides that the Heavenly Book Visitor was traveling their way. No shots were fired for the entire route home. I understand Cary Daniels later told that when he returned, there was dangerous shooting all around. The experience was frightening. However, he finally arrived back at the hospital unscathed and could only praise God for protection."

Lottie breathed a deep sigh, and the weariness of her face touched the tender hearts of each girl.

"Aunt Lottie," Marion spoke with concern sounding in every word,

"I am very thankful you were safe. You are so special to us."

Edith agreed, "You are like part of our family. We are so glad you are safely home."

Rachel's head was nodding in agreement with her sisters' words, "Aunt Lottie, we will never forget all the ways you love us and are helping us grow into strong people."

With her tender smile, Lottie reached out to gather a hand of each girl into her gnarled hands. "My dear girls, you know that this works two ways. You are a true blessing to me." She tightened her grip as best she could and concluded, "The dear Lord has used you to be a balm to my heart and a lift to my weary soul. I realize you must return home tomorrow — but always remember, you have kept your Aunt Lottie young in heart and spirit."

Lottie drew in a deep breath. "Do not ever forget. God has a special purpose for *you*. You seek Him all the days of your life, and He will make of you a special blessing."

Three young girls felt the very presence of God with them in that sacred moment. They carried the memory in their hearts for the rest of their lives. Rachel and her beloved Aunt Lottie had an opportunity for a quiet moment the next day as the sisters were preparing to leave.

Rachel spoke softly, "Aunt Lottie, thank you for helping me see the needs all about me. You helped me know how to think and pray and seek God." Her eyes brimmed with tears, "I know God wants me to serve him here in China. You have helped open my eyes and my heart," and she hugged the frail little woman with the giant heart and spirit. "Aunt Lottie, I will never forget."

The Rest of the Story

Rachel Newton did not forget. She answered God's call on her life. Rachel was appointed to China in 1922 and sailed for north China that

September. She later married Dr. John Dickson, a widowed missionary physician in China. They had one child, Mary. Tragically, John Dickson died of pneumonia just three months after Mary was born. Rachel remained in China and was a teacher. She and young Mary were driven out by the Japanese in 1941 during World War II. Rachel Newton Dickson served as a staff member of the Foreign Mission Board headquarters in Richmond, Virginia, for twenty-two years. She never forgot the profound influence of Lottie Moon on her growing up years.

Extra Credit

The Boxer Rebellion was a scary time for Christians in China in 1900. Look online and in library books to learn how the Boxers got started and explore what happened to the missionaries and other foreigners in China during those months. One of those foreigners was a young geological engineer in Tianjin, North China. He and his wife escaped injury and death during those dangerous months. His name was Herbert Hoover. He later became the thirty-first President of the United States.

Lottie with two young missionaries: Ella Jeter (left) and Jessie Pettigrew (right). Both served for forty years in China.

(9(2

Epilogue

All of China had gone through great turmoil. First, it was terrible famine. Then came a nationwide revolution that resulted in China becoming a republic. Of all the missionaries, Lottie Moon had most internalized China's woes. These were her people, and she felt the burden of China's griefs. Those griefs were stunningly real to her.

Outwardly, Lottie seemed pretty much her usual self at the July annual mission meeting. However, she was noticeably frail and moving slowly. On the other hand, her mind was as keen and sharp as ever. She confided her own problems and sorrows to no one. Though, as usual, she listened compassionately to the needs of each missionary present. At the end of the meeting, Lottie wrote a long and articulate report to the Foreign Mission Board.

Lottie's house and grounds remained full of sick and starving Chinese women who had no one to help them. Lottie not only shared her food with the women, but also spent hours each day attending to their nursing needs. She bound their wounds and bathed their frail bodies. Children came to her door every day, begging for food. She turned no one away. For years now, Lottie, with her own money, had been feeding and caring for those who had nothing. If they couldn't eat, she wouldn't eat.

In sad fact, Lottie soon became so frail that she could no longer think clearly. In a matter of two months, missionaries who saw her were shocked. They began seeking advice and help from other missionaries, especially doctors and nurses.

Lottie Moon's final decline was frighteningly rapid. She had internalized all her personal family sorrows. Sister Edmonia was her closest remaining relative and the most beloved. A letter telling of Edmonia's death struck overwhelming sorrow to her weary heart. Lottie didn't tell a soul but continued as usual to love and help those around her.

The Foreign Mission Board was deeply in debt. That worried her. Lottie sent her remaining inheritance to try to pay off the board's debt. Meanwhile, she found other missionaries who gladly took over responsibility for many of her duties in Tengzhou (*Duhng Joe*). Lottie also found new leaders for all seven of the schools she was directing and turned over her village work to younger missionaries.

Lottie knew that she was becoming more confused every day. In October, she sent for Dr. Adams, asking him to make out a will for her and be its executor. She had a special love for the Adamses. When Floy came to China to marry Dr. Adams, Lottie was in charge of directing their beautiful wedding. Arriving at her door that fall morning, Dr. Adams was shocked to see how rapidly his old friend was failing. Lottie tearfully told him the board was bankrupt, and she had no money either. As they talked, she became increasingly confused.

Dr. Adams asked Jane Lide to come care for her. "Miss Janie" was one of the new young missionaries that Lottie had loved and nurtured. Her heart grieved to see Miss Moon failing and suffering.

Miss Lide took care of all of Lottie's household duties, helping provide for Li Tai Tai (*Lee Tie Tie*), Lottie's beloved longtime cook, as she retired. Janie packed all of Lottie's things, preparing her clothes to take with them when they left for medical help. However, Miss Moon dissolved in tears and could not bring herself to leave. After two weeks, Miss Lide grew more alarmed and asked for help. Nurse Pettigrew, another of Lottie's beloved young single missionaries, came promptly.

Jessie Pettigrew examined Lottie and found a giant carbuncle-like growth at the base of her neck. As she cleaned and dressed the infection, Nurse Pettigrew asked Lottie, "Miss Moon, please tell me what is the matter? What troubles you?"

Lottie wept and answered, "It's troubles in my mind. Oh, I am such a sinner. I am so unworthy." She could no longer explain her grief and sorrow. Lottie grew so confused at one point that she could not keep from worrying over the lingering famine. She wept as she told Nurse Pettigrew, "Just think of all of Mr. Newton's little children, all starving to death."

Miss Pettigrew notified Dr. Gaston at the Laichowfu (*Lie Joe Foo*) hospital, and he came at once. He immediately took Lottie to his home. Worried over Miss Moon's quick deterioration, Dr. Gaston soothed and cared for her. He and other missionary doctors conferred and decided she must return to America. That would be the only hope for saving her life. Nurse Cynthia Miller was soon due for her furlough, and she gladly agreed to accompany their beloved Miss Lottie to medical care in America.

Missionaries decided that Dr. T.O. Hearn, much loved by Lottie Moon, would accompany Lottie and Nurse Cynthia Miller to the port city of Tsingtao (*Ching Dow*) to sail to America. Lottie was upset, saying, "Go to America? But I want to be in Pingtu (*Ping Do*) on my *kang (kahng),* teaching people about God's love for them." Miss Moon was rational just part of each day; the rest of the time she could not understand reality.

Early the December morning of departure, Dr. Hearn and Nurse Miller gently put Lottie on a cushioned cot for the journey to Tsingtao and the harbor where her ship waited. As they tenderly placed her on the soft bed, Dr. Hearn soothingly said, "Just lay down, dear Miss Moon." Immediately, Lottie sat up and retorted, "I will not lay down, sir, but I will lie down." There was a hint of a smile on her lips. Lottie the English teacher was showing her spirit yet again.

Dr. Hearn arranged everything possible for her comfort. Nurse and patient shared a cabin. Day and night, Cynthia Miller tenderly cared for Lottie. She later wrote, "Miss Moon gave up all will to live as her ship, the *Manchuria,* sailed out of Chinese waters. She grew quieter and weaker by the hour."

Nurse Miller told of the final days of Lottie Moon's life. When Lottie felt able to talk and was clear in her mind, she always spoke of heavenly things. She asked her nurse, "Will you tell me why it is that Christian people are so good?"

Cynthia replied that it must be the spirit of God in their hearts.

In a weak voice, Lottie requested, "Why don't you pray for Him to come and fill up my heart?"

Miss Miller assured her that was exactly what she was doing. "I am praying that He will come and give you peace and comfort."

Lottie tenderly smiled, "You are? Well, He has come. Jesus is here right now. When He comes in, He drives out all evil, you know."

Christmas Eve arrived. All that day Lottie was quiet, occasionally sleeping, then rousing. Later that final evening of Lottie Moon's life, she roused and whispered, "Jesus loves me, this I know," and then sang the entire verse of her favorite hymn. Lottie next requested that her nurse sing "Simply Trusting Every Day." Miss Miller sang it like a lullaby.

On Christmas Eve 1912, as the midnight hour approached, Lottie Moon opened her eyes one more time. She smiled and looked around. Then looking upward, she raised her hands in a joined fist. This was the loving Chinese gesture of greeting a dear one. Time and again, a smile would cross her face and she would give a slight nod and another movement of her joined hands in greeting to yet another dear one.

Nurse Miller later told of those final sacred moments of Lottie Moon's life. It was as if the gates of heaven were opening. Miss Moon was seeing before her eyes those friends who had preceded her to heaven. She was greeting, one by one, Chinese men, women, and children she had led to know of God's love. Nurse Miller recalled the last words Lottie spoke — a whispered, "Jesus Loves Me." Then Lottie Moon closed her eyes one final time. The Heavenly Book Visitor was now in the presence of God, the one whose gift of love and eternal life she had so long and faithfully shared.

Historical Note

There is no clear medical answer as to what actually caused Lottie Moon's death. The team of missionary doctors made the decision to try to get her to America before her frail body gave out. In the United States, doctors would have the equipment and expertise to care for her. When she died in the harbor at Kobe, Japan, Japanese law dictated that the body must be cremated. Nurse Cynthia Miller took back to Virginia the small silver urn containing her earthly remains.

Medical people have puzzled for years over the cause of death. Certainly, malnutrition had to be a factor. Famine was widespread in China in 1911 and 1912. Lottie was so devoted to her people, the Chinese, that she spent her time, energy, and resources feeding them. She gave little thought to herself. Miss Moon had recently learned of her beloved sister Edmonia's death, but she shared the news with no one. Instead, she grieved silently.

Lottie was horrified to learn that the Foreign Mission Board was deeply in debt. She sent all she could of her remaining inheritance to try to bail them out. Famine and revolution had added to her burden.

Then Nurse Pettigrew discovered the infected and unusual carbuncle at the base of her neck. This may have had a direct neurological effect on her brain. Maybe it was a combination of all the possible factors. No one but God Himself has the answer. What we do know is that she willingly gave of herself in order to bring to saving grace each person she met. Her love for China was returned in full measure as the many believers she had brought to Christ said over and over, "How she loved us."

*1915 Monument to Lottie Moon, erected by the believers who knew and loved her.
With Pastor Qin and Baptist friends from America, 2008.*

THE LEGACY

Christmas Eve 1912 was not the end of the work and influence of Lottie Moon. It was actually the true beginning of her wonderful legacy. Lottie's influence reached far beyond the grave. She became a prime example of a believer whose life was truly a living sacrifice. Lottie Moon left behind living monuments through the lives of the many hundreds whom she led to faith during her thirty-nine years in China.

Now into a third century since the beginning of her China ministry in 1873, Lottie Moon has literally become a household name among Baptists around the world. She represents all that is noble and true in ministry, in caring, and in loving others. She is a symbol of service and sacrifice.

Lottie Moon began life as an heiress in Virginia. Her life ended without enough money left to pay her way back to her native land. But that life left a matchless legacy to all of us who share the challenge of the Great Commission with her. Lottie took that commission to heart and became "Exhibit A" for courage, commitment, dedication, and bravery. The congregation of her Monument Street Church in Tengzhou (*Duhng Joe*), now known as Peng Lai (*Puhng Lie*), erected a monument in her memory. It translates: "To bequeath the love of Miss Lottie Moon, an American missionary." The monument sums it up: "The Tengzhou church remembers forever."

The north China mission felt lost without the leadership and loving presence of their beloved Miss Lottie. The missionaries said, "She is the one who would tell us how the Chinese would look at this thing or that;

therefore, we don't want to do anything that will hinder the Master's cause." All the missionaries' kids mourned their treasured "Aunt Lottie." The Chinese asked, time and again, "When will the Heavenly Book Visitor come again?"

When the believers in China learned that their beloved Miss Moon, Li Ti Au (*Lee Tea Awh*) had died, they didn't talk about her brilliant mind. They didn't mention her marvelous ability with the Chinese language or her many skills. They simply said, "How she loved us."

In 1918, Annie Armstrong, the retired first secretary (director) of national Woman's Missionary Union, suggested that Baptists name the annual Christmas offering for world missions after Lottie Moon. It was Lottie Moon who, some thirty years earlier, pleaded with Baptists in America to begin a Christmas offering for missions. Lottie felt Christmas time was most appropriate, since that was the time of year gifts are given to others in honor of the greatest gift, God's Son. The Lottie Moon Christmas Offering, named for a tiny little woman with a giant heart, became the single largest missions offering in the world.

An astounding and eternal tribute to the life and work of Lottie Moon can be found in the fact that during just the last year of her life, 2,358 persons were baptized in north China. Two months after her death, the *Foreign Mission Journal* wrote of her passing and spoke of her remarkable life. The article dubbed her, "The best man among our missionaries."

Harry Ayers, a prominent newspaper publisher in Alabama, was one of the MKs so richly impacted by Lottie Moon's life. When Miss Moon returned to America on the last of her only two furloughs, Harry, a teenager, traveled with her. He was coming back to go to college. He was deeply influenced through his teenage years by "Aunt Lottie." She had the most brilliant mind and broadest education of anyone he was ever to meet. He called her a "pioneer torchbearer" and "a spiritual benediction." Harry declared he had never met another person so richly endowed with abilities. And, Harry added, "She is also one who deserted a Virginia mansion to live in a Chinese hut by the side of a road and become a friend to man."

Lottie Moon would be astounded to think that a worldwide offering was named for her. She would never want the praise. She would, however, cherish the fact that people were giving out of generous hearts to tell the good news to those who have never heard. Lottie never worried about herself or her personal wants. Her concern was for those who needed the message of God's love and His gift of Salvation.

In the mid 1890s, when she was about fifty years old and was exhausted at the end of each day, Lottie declared, "I begin to feel the effects of age. I have felt the uncertainty of life very keenly of late. However, I have a firm conviction that I am immortal till my work is done." Lottie Moon's remarkable story is a basic part of our shared Baptist missions history. It has become ours to pass on to the generation that follows ours. The remarkable and loving legacy left by Lottie Moon inspires us to give, to pray, to go.

Lottie Moon at age 30

Bibliography

Books and Articles

Allen, Catherine B. *The New Lottie Moon Story*. Broadman Press (Nashville, TN). 1980.

Ayers, Harry M. "Lottie Moon As I Knew Her," *Royal Service*. WMU (Birmingham, AL). December 1935 (5-6).

"W.C. Newton Dies," *Foreign Mission News*. (Richmond, VA). December 24, 1966 (4-5).

Harper, Keith. *Send the Light: Lottie Moon's Letters and Other Writings*. Mercer Press (Macon, GA). 2002.

International Mission Board (Richmond, VA). Numerous records from archives, pictures, letters, and reports from China.

Moore, John Allen. "Her Journey Ends," *Commission* (Richmond, VA). January 1986 (76-78).

Johnson, Julia Toy. "For the Heathen Helper," *Heathen Helper* (Louisville, KY). May 1888 (4-5).

Southern Baptist Historical Library and Archives (Nashville, TN). Numerous records and documents related to North China and Lottie Moon.

Virginia Baptist Historical Society (Richmond, VA). January 22, 1895.

CPSIA information can be obtained
at www.ICGtesting.com
Printed in the USA
BVHW092056070623
665486BV00005B/10

9 781955 295352